Om tare

tuttare

ture mama

ayur jñana

punye pushtim kuru soha

White Tara Mantra

Easy Healing Drinks from the Wisdom of Ayurveda

Delicious and Nourishing Recipes for All Seasons

AMADEA MORNINGSTAR

Photography by RENEE LYNN

AYURVEDA POLARITY THERAPY
& YOGA INSTITUTE
SANTA FE, NEW MEXICO

Ayurveda Polarity Therapy & Yoga Institute
7 Avenida Vista Grande #186
Santa Fe, New Mexico 87508
www.AyurvedaPolarityYoga.com

Some material has previously appeared in *EASY HEALING DRINKS FROM THE WISDOM OF AYURVEDA: Delicious and Nourishing Winter Recipes eBook* and *EASY HEALING DRINKS FROM THE WISDOM OF AYURVEDA: Cleansing and Sustaining Recipes eBook*.

DISCLAIMER:
This book is not intended to treat, diagnose or prescribe. The information contained herein is in no way to be considered as a substitute for your own good common sense, or as a substitute for a consultation with a duly licensed health care professional.

Published in the United States of America

Designed by Cynthia Bancale; cover design by Leslie Waltzer, Crowfoot Design; production by Elizabeth Carovillano

Printed & Distributed by Nataraj Books, Inc., www.natarajbooks.com with biodegradable ink

ISBN: 978-0-9987542-5-3 (paperback)

Library of Congress Control Number: 2018935504

Publisher's Cataloging-in-Publication Data
Morningstar, Amadea (Ayurveda author)
Easy Healing Drinks from the Wisdom of Ayurveda: Delicious and Nourishing Recipes for All Seasons/
Amadea Morningstar; photography by Renee Lynn; Foreword by Dr. Vasant Lad.

First edition.
160 pages
Includes index.
1. Vegetarian cooking   2. Seasonal Cooking   3. Medicine, Ayurvedic
4. Healing Drinks

To the life giving Earth

and to Vedic wisdom

for the benefit of all sentient beings

with much gratitude from us both.

~ Renee and Amadea

To my root teachers, to all of my teachers,

especially Dr. Vasant Lad,

to my colleagues, clients, and students,

and to you, kind reader.

~ Amadea

Contents

Foreword by Dr. Vasant Lad

Ayurveda is a timeless, Vedic, wisdom healing for mankind that speaks a great deal about the health of the individual. The birth of the individual is the birth of the universe. Sānkhya's philosophy of creation tells of two forces: *Purusha*, which is choiceless passive awareness and *Prakruti*, the primordial matter, the creative potential. These two divine, dynamic forces are timeless and eternal. Before creation, Purusha and Prakruti were merged together. For the purpose of creation, after the big bang, Prakruti separated from Purusha and the result was a pulsation of cosmic prāna, called *matrishwara* prāna. Matrishwara prāna is the vibration of creation of pranic energy that is the bridge between Purusha and Prakruti. Its first expression is *Mahad*, which is supreme intelligence. Next created is *Ahamkāra* (individual intelligence), and then *sattva*, *rajas*, and *tamas* and the whole of creation.

According to Ayurveda, in our body, every single cell is the center of awareness. There is a micro-purusha in every single cell. Every cell has RNA/DNA (Prakruti), which is your blue print or genetic code. This single cell is a functional unit of the body. It has Purusha and Prakruti, and there is a continuous flow of cellular intelligence, which is called *prāna*. Prāna is the life force.

Ayurveda discusses the five elements: Ether, Air, Fire, Water and Earth. The biological combination of the five elements is Ether, the space within the cell; Air, the movement of the cytoplasm; Fire, the cellular metabolic activity; Water in the plasma, serum, and cytoplasm; and Earth is composed mainly of the cell membrane. These five elements play an important role in the structural aspect of the single cell.

As for physiological functions, the biological combination of Ether and Air is *vāta dosha*, which is the principal of movement. Fire and Water is *pitta dosha*, the energy of transformation of food into microchyle. Earth and Water are *kapha*, the building block materials of the body. Vāta, pitta, kapha are the dynamic organization of the body. They are the functional principles that govern each individual's unique cycle of physiology or constitution.

According to Ayurveda, an Ayurvedic physician does an assessment of the individual's *prakruti* and *vikruti* to determine the person's constitution and the present, altered status of the dosha. Our bodies are constantly undergoing changes because of aging, wear and tear to the body, seasonal changes, dietetic changes, emotional changes, changes in one's job, and changes in the environment. We are continually experiencing these fluctuations and, because of them, our prakruti (constitution) is gradually imbalanced. This changed status of the doshas is called vikruti. The prakruti-vikruti paradigm is the basic paradigm of Ayurveda. The Ayurvedic approach to health describes how we can return our vikruti dosha back to our prakruti dosha's balanced state. Ayurveda explains how proper diet, lifestyle, *panchakarma* detoxification and *rasayana* (rejuvenation) programs will restore this balance. This is the ancient Ayurvedic approach.

Amadea Morningstar has written this wonderful book, *Easy Healing Drinks from the Wisdom of Ayurveda*, which shares the health-promoting principles of Ayurveda. I have known Amadea since 1980. During those days, my friend Lenny Blank, Amadea, and my whole family lived together in Santa Fe. I observed closely Amadea Morningstar's great knowledge. She is a nutrition educator, knows polarity, practices yoga, has studied Ayurveda, and is a great spiritual person. She has been teaching cooking and nutrition since the 1980's.

Her approach to healing through these healing drinks is based upon the Ayurvedic principles of *rasa*, *vīrya*, and *vipāka*. Rasa is the taste, vīrya is the energy, and vipāka is the post-digestive effect. And *prabhāva* is the specific action of the herbs, food, grain, vegetables, and fruits.

This book has practical wisdom for practitioners. It shows how to balance your vāta, pitta, or kapha doshas according to your unique constitution. To bring our vikruti dosha back to the balanced state of prakruti dosha is the basic principal of Ayurveda. Amadea has created these wonderful formulas: smoothies, teas, vegetable juices, root teas, almond milk, and golden milk. They are very fascinating and she includes information on how they work on your physiology according to the systems of Ayurveda. These drinks deliver nutrition to many levels of the body's systems.

An example is Rasa Tea. I like her concept because rasa is the body's plasma, it is blood serum. Rasa is also the taste; the six tastes of sweet, sour, salty, bitter, pungent, and astringent. Rasa is the juice, rasa is the essence, and rasa is the melody. And this tea supports the rasa dhātu in the body.

Every tea, juice, or herbal decoction/concoction passes through the mouth, into the stomach and on to the GI (gastrointestinal) tract. It is mixed with the digestive enzymes and it enters into the microchyle. This substance is *āhāra rasa*, which is the food precursor of all bodily tissues. As it moves through the digestive process, it becomes *sthāyi rasa* (mature rasa dhātu that nourishes the rasa dhātu) and *asthāyi rasa*, the precursor nutrient for rakta dhātu. Her herbal teas work through the asthāyi rasa and then work on sthāyi rasa. Smoothies work directly on the sthāyi rasa, bringing nutrition to the rasa dhātu.

Easy Healing Drinks from the Wisdom of Ayurveda will be a very useful guide for new readers. People are aware of the three doshas but many are not aware of the seven *dhātus*. This book will definitely help the reader to understand their own dhātus, that is, their own biological tissues which may be weak and not well-nourished. These healing drinks make up a practical guide, not only in balancing your doshas, but to nourish your dhātus. Nourishing your dhātus will then yield into building *ojas, tejas,* and prāna. Healthy ojas, tejas, and prāna will bring you cellular health.

Love and Light,

Vasant Lad, BAM&S, MASc, Ayurvedic Physician

Author of *Ayurveda: Science of Self-Healing, Textbook of Ayurveda* series and more

Winter: An Introduction to Ayurveda

A direct experience of Ayurveda

Aimee rushed into the beginning of the workshop on a cold winter morning late last year. She was starving and wondered if there was time to run out and grab a bite to eat before class started. My co-facilitator and I took one look at her and said together, "No, let us feed you here, we've got plenty." We put a mug of hot tea in her hand and heated up a bowl of warm food. Aimee is a bright lean strong young farmer by profession and spends a lot of time outside in nature. At the end of the weekend (which included warm delicious food and some of the recipes here), she shared an epiphany. It was the first time in months that she actually felt warm inside! Usually she was always cold. While she had a keen sense of the seasons from her work, it was the first time she realized that she could eat with the seasons in a simple, Ayurvedic way. She was ready for this new adventure in drinking and eating. It supported her body and felt great.

What you'll receive

Discover in this book how to support your own health – or regain deeper health – with simple, delicious elixirs. They're easy to make and even easier to drink! Ayurveda is an ancient, time-tested system of healing from India, that has proven itself to be highly adaptable to current times and needs. It works with the season as well as the individual.

Hydrate yourself and start the day right. Sometimes you think you may be hungry, when really you are dehydrated. In the West, it's customary to start a meal with iced, cold water regardless of the season. This inhibits digestive fire and slows healthy metabolism, especially in winter. Ayurveda uses opposites to balance and the warming drinks that follow are specifically designed for the chilly winter season. Warm drinks in winter nourish your tissues, support your digestive fire, and are easy to absorb.

Understanding the basics of Ayurveda

If you're new to Ayurveda, it is a nature-based system of healing that originated in East India more than 5,000 years ago. Sanskrit for "the science of life", Ayurveda is an invitation to discover the science and art of being healthy within your own life. You can adapt it to meet your needs, and you may find yourself adapting your lifestyle to integrate its wisdom. In working with this ancient healing art, you rely on the five elements of nature: earth, water, fire, air and space. These five elements are distilled in all of life, including our bodies, into three basic biological energies known as the *doshas*: *Kapha*, *Pitta*, and *Vata*. Everyone has all three of these doshas, yet in different proportions. To get an idea of your constitution, here is a trustworthy, interactive test: https://www.banyanbotanicals.com/info/prakruti-quiz/

You can directly explore Vata, Pitta, and Kapha in hands-on ways for yourself. They each have unique qualities (*gunas*) that show up within you. If you're feeling dry, you are experiencing one attribute of Vata, whose other qualities include cool, light, mobile, and fast. If you're hot, this is one strong quality of Pitta, whose additional attributes are sharp, light, oily, and moist. If you're feeling noticeably heavy, this relates to Kapha, which can also manifest as cool, dense, slow, and steady. What if you are feeling dry, hot and heavy all at once? All three doshas are appearing at your doorstep! This is possible. What now?

Remember opposites are healing in Ayurveda. When dry and thirsty, you can enjoy moistening drinks. If hot, try cooler beverages. If you're feeling heavy, we'd suggest you consume something lighter. A lighter drink could be made from a clear broth, while a heavier one could include dairy or nuts. You can directly respond to your needs by choosing the appropriate balancing foods and qualities. In the fictitious example above, you could respond to dry, hot and heavy with moist, cool, and light.

The following recipes let you know how each drink supports each dosha. Combining the attributes in healing ways can be a creative activity, like painting with a full palette of colors. Feel free to use these recipes as the basis for your own improvisation.

Many of you reading this may already have a fine-tuned, experiential understanding of the doshas of Ayurveda. If so, we'd like to invite you to expand your knowledge further with some of the more subtle aspects of Ayurvedic physiology that comprise the foundation for an Ayurvedic practitioner's therapeutic choices. We'd like you to meet the dhatus in a skillful way.

What are the dhatus? In ancient India, the *dhatus* were known as the indispensable tissues. Without them, we could not live! These seven essential tissues for life and health were and are used in the deeper experiential applications of rejuvenation and *rasayana*. Without a clear grasp of the dhatus, we often deplete our own tissues

heedlessly to keep up with some imagined idea of what we're supposed to accomplish in a day. This blatant disregard for our own tissues has a lot in common with how some corporations are treating the earth. It's there, let's take it, with no regard for long term consequences or respect for nature. With a wise comprehension of the dhatus, we can recognize an essential tissue and its needs before it lands us in the ER or prostrate on our couches. Plus, this understanding gives us the opportunity to respect Mother Nature in our own lives and bodies on a daily basis.

Rasa	Plasma, liquid blood & lymph
Rakta	Red blood cells
Mamsa	Muscle
Meda	Fat
Asthi	Bone
Majja	Bone marrow, nerves & fascia
Artava	Female reproductive system
Shukra	Male reproductive system

THE DHATUS: ESSENTIAL TISSUES

Within this framework of the seven essential categories of tissues are woven the organs and other endocrine glands. In Sanskrit, *dhatu* literally means building block, or that which holds potency. *Ojas*, our vital immunity, is built from all the dhatus.

When we exhaust ourselves, we deplete our tissues and shake the foundations of our health. The healing recipes you'll find here let you discover how to gently revive them.

How the dhatus dance together

In the dance of nurturance, our bodies digest and absorb whatever nourishment they can from the digestive tract, the gateway to the dhatus. From the digestive tract, nutrients first enter rasa, or plasma, the liquid part of our blood. Rasa/plasma is the starting point for the nourishment and cleansing of all the other essential tissues. Rasa/plasma carries nutrients to every other tissue and carries wastes away. Whatever we don't need or can't digest and absorb is eliminated in the feces, urine, and sweat, the three primary waste products or *malas*.

Each of the seven tissues nourishes the next tissue in a cosmic dance. *Rasa* (plasma) feeds *rakta* (red blood cells), which sustains *mamsa* (muscle). The energy of mamsa flows into *meda* (fat), which moistens *asthi* (bone). Within asthi resides *majja*, the bone marrow. Majja also encompasses our nerves and fascia. Majja influences *artava* and *shukra* dhatus, the reproductive tissues of women and men respectively. (While these last two are separate dhatus, for our purposes here they will share the category of the seventh dhatu.) Here Ayurveda presents an ancient twist on modern psychoneuroendocrinology in the clinical study of hormone changes and how they affect human behavior. Thousands of years ago, Ayurveda taught that the nervous system affects reproductive behavior, and vice versa.

Each dhatu provides nourishment to the next and each has a characteristic way of keeping clear. For example, when rasa/plasma becomes congested, it releases its waste as mucus. We sneeze, we cough, we clear our throats. Rasa also receives help in maintaining its balance and health through the processes of perspiration and urination. For more information about specific foods and herbs to support each dhatu, see *The Ayurvedic Guide to Polarity Therapy* (Morningstar).

The point here is you may think you have a problem with your muscles. An Ayurvedic practitioner would look at you and ask, Is the digestive system absorbing what the muscles need? Is there healthy rasa/plasma to accept these nutrients and pass them on to the muscles? This same method of thinking is applied to all tissues and health challenges. The good news is you can nourish and cleanse your essential tissues with food and herbs.

About digestion

The gateway to our essential tissues is our digestive tract. If you can't digest a food or spice, it won't be absorbed. If it isn't absorbed, it cannot nourish you or your tissues. For this reason, Ayurveda puts a big emphasis on how digestible a food or meal is. Because we're all somewhat different from one another, what one person digests well is not necessarily what makes another person's gut happy. For this reason, Ayurveda recommends different foods and lifestyles for different people. It's vital to design nourishment to accommodate the needs of your doshas as well as your dhatus. This need not be as complicated as you might imagine! There are many easy ways to nourish and refresh your tissues and doshas starting with the recipes here. Remember, from an Ayurvedic perspective, digestion is the gateway to health.

About rasa

Liquid nourishment specifically strengthens rasa. Rasa is what gives us our juiciness; it's the moist liquid portion of our circulatory and lymph systems. It is both the plasma and lymph fluid. Like a river, it carries nourishment and transports wastes. For this reason, rasa dhatu, the essential plasma, is all about flow, as well as moisture. The healing drink recipes here support this flow and hydration.

When rasa is depleted, we become dehydrated. Without rasa, we can become dry and crispy. Without rasa, essential moisture cannot be delivered to every cell that needs it, and wastes can pile up as *ama* (undigested toxins) in the cells and passageways of the body. Rather than being like some radiant, large, shining lake, we may feel like a small, over-heated puddle.

To support your rasa and all your tissues, including ojas, your vital immunity, we offer you easily digested, nutritious drinks, many of them plant-based, all gluten-free.

The importance of working with the season

Individuals have different qualities or *gunas*. So do seasons. As this is being written, it's winter, which is cold, heavy, moist and slow. To counter these attributes, we want to offer you nourishment that is warm, easy to digest, and enlivening. You notice we didn't say dry. Because we want to feed your tissues, with rasa/plasma as the starting point, we need to give you enough moisture to revive and enliven your rasa. The appropriate nourishing drinks can make a big difference in your health each season.

Make your recipes successfully

Let's look at the first recipe, IMMUNE BOOSTING CCF TEA. Gather what you need and follow the simple directions on how to put the drink together. "Effects" lets you know how this recipe impacts each dosha. "This drink supports" tells you what dhatus are impacted by this beverage, as well as other benefits. In some recipes, there may be "Comments" that give you more information about the specific healing properties of the drink, or "Notes" about who contributed to its creation. In many recipes, there is the extra bonus of Variations.

We emphasize organic ingredients whenever possible, both for the health of the planet and you. As we write this, less than 5% of the Ayurvedic herbal market is organic. Pesticides and other contaminants are common; their adverse effects are well understood. For daily use, or when rejuvenating or cleansing, organic is important. Most herbal ingredients are organic and ground, unless specified otherwise as whole seeds, petals, or roots.

The Appendices at the back offer further key information about Ayurveda and Western nutrition. Discover how different attributes impact your doshas and digestive fire. How specific flavors can influence your doshic balance. Learn what dark leafy greens are best for whom. Explore the Resources when you want to expand your adventure beyond these pages. In the Resources Book section, you can also find all the Inline citations. Each citation in *Easy Healing Drinks* gives an author and a page number, ex: (Tirtha, 134). This example relates to Tirtha's *Ayurveda Encyclopedia*, page 134.

See the Acknowledgments for all the generous people who have been involved with us in this creative adventure. We especially wish to acknowledge you, kind reader, for joining us here. Healing wishes, gladness and respect to you.

Enjoy your journey to vibrant health!

Amadea Morningstar and Renee Lynn
January 2018, Santa Fe, New Mexico

Winter Recipes

Ojas is our vital immunity, our cushion.
This tea helps build and protect it!

IMMUNE BOOSTING CCF TEA *YEAR-ROUND*

Time: 15 minutes
Makes: 2 cups

2 1/4 cups water
1/2 teaspoon each:
- whole cumin seeds
- whole coriander seeds
- whole fennel seeds
- fenugreek seeds
1/4 teaspoon turmeric

1/8 teaspoon ground cinnamon
   or cardamom
1 – 2 inches astragalus root
   (optional)
1 thin slice of ginger, chopped

Bring the water to a boil in a stainless steel pot. Add all the spices.
Simmer ten minutes or more. Strain. Drink 2 cups per day, with love.

Effects: calms Vata and Kapha, neutral for Pitta

This drink supports: digestion, plasma, blood, female reproduction, and ojas!

*Comments: Astragalus is excellent for the tail end of a flu or as prevention.
Skip it, though, if you are in the early stages of an acute, infectious state.*

VARIATION: Make a whole pot of **IMMUNE BOOSTING CCF TEA.**

Serves 12 with 3 1/2 quarts water, 1 Tablespoon each: whole cumin seeds, whole coriander seeds, whole fennel seeds, and fenugreek seeds. 1 teaspoon turmeric, 1 cinnamon stick or 3 whole cardamom pods, 1 stick of astragalus root (optional), 1/2 - 1 inch slice of fresh ginger, chopped. Follow directions above.

VARIATION: CLASSIC CUMIN-CORIANDER-FENNEL TEA (CCF Tea)

As above, steep 1 Tablespoon each: whole cumin, coriander, and fennel seeds in one quart of boiled water.

Effects: tridoshic.

Supports: excellent digestion. It is also quite diuretic. When your digestive organs seem to be dancing to different rhythms and melodies, remember this classic support.

LUSCIOUS LEMON TEA *YEAR-ROUND*

Time: 5 minutes
Makes: one cup

1 cup water
1/4 teaspoon organic lemon zest, finely grated
1/4 teaspoon fresh ginger, finely grated
1 Tablespoon organic lemon juice (juice of 1/2 lemon)
1 pinch (1/16 teaspoon) ground cardamom or ground cinnamon
1/2 - 1 teaspoon raw honey

Boil the water. As it's heating, wash the lemon and finely grate some peel for the zest.
On the same grater, grate the ginger. Squeeze the lemon for its juice.
Put these and the remaining ingredients in a tea cup. Stir in the hot water, let it sit a moment,
then add the honey. Enjoy.

Effects: calms Vata, in excess can aggravate Pitta & Kapha. Lime is a fine cooling alternative for Pitta.
With stevia, Kapha could have this twice a week with a neutral effect.

This tea supports: plasma, blood, alkalizing.

SWEET VARIATIONS: For your sweet options, try raw honey for Vata or Kapha, coconut sugar, maple syrup or organic agave syrup for Pitta or Vata, stevia for Kapha.

EXTRA EASY VARIATION: Just use hot water, lemon juice, cardamom or cinnamon, and sweetener.
As one taster commented: "Easy, tastes good, looks good, no challenge, and I like it."

VATA VARIATION: You can add one additional teaspoon of lemon juice if you're a Vata and like it tart.

ESSENTIAL RASA TEA   *YEAR-ROUND*

Time: 35 minutes or less
Makes: 3 cups plus

1 quart water
1 Tablespoon fenugreek seeds
1 Tablespoon fennel seeds
1 Tablespoon dried peppermint or marshmallow root
1 teaspoon licorice root, chopped or powdered (optional)
1 thin slice fresh ginger root (optional)
1 teaspoon to 1 Tablespoon flax seeds per cup (optional)

Boil water in a medium stainless steel pot. Put all the herbs in a one-quart heat-proof glass Mason jar. Pour the water over the herbs and steep for 30 minutes or more.

Before serving, strain the tea. It's easy at this point to add extra flax seeds directly into your cup before pouring the Essential Rasa tea into it. This is for people who like gloppy Omega 3-rich, immune-boosting, mood-soothing foods. You can eat the soaked seeds with a spoon when you get to the bottom of your drink (if you're not a Pitta!)

Drink 1 - 2 cups per day, the larger amount if you are in dry conditions.

Effects: balances all doshas, tridoshic

This tea supports: plasma, nerves, female & male reproductive systems, lactation, ojas.

Comments: Rasa/plasma is the raw ingredient for every other dhatu. For nourishment and hydration, Amadea recommends this tea almost daily in her practice.

ESSENTIAL RASA TEA MIX: Makes 28 cups or 2 weeks' worth, using 1 Tablespoon/cup.

In a large bowl, stir together 1/2 cup each: fenugreek seeds, fennel seeds, peppermint or chopped marshmallow root, and 1 Tablespoon licorice root, chopped or powdered. Store in a glass jar in a cool, dark place. When you are ready to make your Essential Rasa Tea, bring the water to a boil with a thin slice of ginger, add 1 level Tablespoon of the spice tea mix per cup, and simmer for ten minutes. If you add flax seeds, you can add them to your cup on serving.

VARIATIONS: In hypertension, skip the licorice. If your blood pressure is normal or low, you can use as much as 1 Tablespoon per quart of tea, as a great support for the adrenals. Licorice helps hold moisture in the body, yet it can aggravate hypertension and water retention for the same reason. Flax seeds are an excellent laxative, yet Pitta may find their slimy quality too laxative for comfort.

INTERNET RECOVERY TEA *YEAR-ROUND*

Time: 20 minutes
Makes: 2 quarts = 8 cups

2 quarts water
1 Tablespoon raspberry leaf (or 1 bag raspberry leaf tea)
1/4 cup rose petals
2 Tablespoons dried peppermint (or 2 bags peppermint tea)
1 Tablespoon dried brahmi (*Bacopa*) *
2 teaspoons shankhapushpi powder *
1 thin slice fresh ginger root

In a stainless steel saucepan, bring water to a boil. Add the herbs, stir, turn off the heat, cover. Infuse for five minutes or until it smells friendly. Strain immediately. Unlike many of the teas here, this is an infusion rather than a decoction. If you like your tea stronger, let it sit until it is the flavor you enjoy. Watch out though! It can get bitter the longer it rests. Drink up to 2 cups per day, as needed. Sweeten with honey if you like.

Effects: tridoshic, calms Vata, Pitta and Kapha beautifully.

This therapeutic tea supports: the nervous system in particular; in addition, plasma and female & male reproductive systems.

Comments: Take a break from the internet and Smart phones to heal any dosha, especially Vata and Pitta. If the 24/7 quality has lured you in, to the detriment of your nervous system and basic sanity, consider turning the web off and having a cup of this tea to reset your wisdom link. If you can get yourself out in nature as you drink it, great!

Brahmi/bacopa is a time-honored way to revive mental clarity and memory, and Shankhapushpi is unrivaled in its ability to calm over wrought nerves without a heavy sedative effect. For those of us with very aware nervous systems, it can help us relax. Banyan Botanicals is a good source for shankhapushpi and bacopa. While neither of these has any contraindications, caution would be advised with anti-epileptic, anti-depressant, or sedative medications, as these are their traditional uses (Pole, 269, 150).

*VARIATION: If you haven't got shankhapushpi or bacopa, use an equal amount of lemon balm (*Melissa*) in place of either of these two.

Nice, quick, nourishing shake for extra energy when you need it.

CINNAMON DATE SHAKE   *YEAR-ROUND*

Time: 15 minutes
Makes: one cup

8 – 10 raw almonds, soaked overnight and peeled
2 – 5 pitted dates (depending on how sweet you want it),
    coarsely chopped
1 cup water
1/8 teaspoon ground cinnamon
1/8 teaspoon ground nutmeg
1/16 teaspoon ground cloves

Grind the soaked, peeled almonds in a blender as finely as you can. Add the rest of the ingredients; blend together until the drink is as creamy as possible. Pour the shake into your cup. Unless you have a high-powered Vitamix, your humble blender may leave some stray chunks of sweet date and almond on the bottom. Chew them up; enjoy.

Nice for the middle of the afternoon when you start to get starving. If you like, make it a TO GO ITEM: pour it into a jar, put the lid on, take it with you for when you're hungry.

Effects: calms Vata & Pitta every day, fine for Kapha once a week.

This drink supports: adrenals, energy, reproduction. It's a gently building aphrodisiac.

Note: With appreciation to Susana Andrews of the Ayurvedic Institute, who wisely suggested a snack similar to this as I was eating my way toward panchakarma there.

QUICK VARIATION: If you haven't soaked almonds overnight, you can put them in a heat-proof jar to soak with boiled water for fifteen minutes, then peel. While not as settling to Vata and Pitta as the overnight soak, it is much more calming for these doshas than skipping this drink entirely!

QUICK VARIATION: You can cheat and use 1 Tablespoon raw almond butter in place of the soaked almonds. A little heavier with a little less prana, it does take less time.

ROSY BEET SMOOTHIE

Sweet and spicy, this brilliant magenta drink builds blood and tonifies the liver.

Time: 20 – 25 minutes
Makes: 2 cups, serves 2

1 cup coarsely chopped raw beets (leave the peel on for extra minerals)
1 1/2 cups water
1 teaspoon lemon zest (finely grated organic lemon peel)
1 teaspoon ground coriander
1/8 - 1/4 teaspoon pippali (or dash of black pepper)
1 cup plain yogurt (we use sheep)

Boil the water in a stainless steel saucepan. Add the beets, lemon zest and coriander. Simmer covered until the beets are tender, about 15 – 20 minutes. Process until smooth in a blender, let it sit for a moment to cool a bit. Add the yogurt and pippali. Serve!

Effects: calms Vata enormously, mildly increases Pitta, neutral for Kapha.

This drink supports: digestion, red blood cells; it's alkalizing, strengthening and building.

Comments: Both ROSY BEET SMOOTHIE *and* ZESTY LEMONGRASS CARROT SMOOTHIE *are great in fall and winter, or any time you want to ground and direct Vata energy downward. In Ayurveda, food combining is an important part of optimizing digestion. For example, yogurt is not combined with fruit. Here in an exception to the rule, lemon peel supports the healing action of beets and coriander, promotes bile flow, detoxifies Pitta, and regulates liver, pancreas, and spleen functions (Tirtha, 131). Yogurt combines well with the beet and spices; it is best eaten before sunset to keep your channels open.*

ZESTY LEMONGRASS CARROT SMOOTHIE

Add some radiant phytonutrients to your day!

Time: 15 minutes
Makes 3 (1-cup) servings

2 cups water
3 – 4 medium carrots, scrubbed well (2 cups)
1 teaspoon to 1 Tablespoon fresh ginger, peeled and chopped
1 teaspoon fresh turmeric, chopped (optional)
Pinch of salt

1 - 3 drops lemongrass essential oil, food grade (I use Do Terra for its fresh flavor)
1/2 teaspoon ground coriander
1/4 teaspoon each ground cumin and cardamom
1/2 cup yogurt (optional)

Heat the water to a boil in a medium stainless steel pot. Break the carrots in a few pieces and add to the pot. If you're in a hurry, feel free to chop the carrots in smaller pieces to reduce cooking time, or if you are in a real rush, you can grate them. Keep simmering as you add the ginger, lemongrass essential oil, spices and salt. Cover and simmer until the carrots are tender, about 10 minutes.

Take the pot off the burner and blend until smooth. I use an immersion blender put directly into the hot brew. It's quick and easy. Once smooth, let the drink sit for a moment to cool before adding the yogurt for extra protein and minerals. Blend again. The yogurt creates a lovely melon color. Serve hot.

Effects: without yogurt, calms Vata and Kapha, neutral for Pitta.

With yogurt, very calming to Vata, neutral for Pitta and Kapha.

This drink supports: plasma, immunity, and ojas. With yogurt, it also supports bones and nerves.

Notes: With much appreciation to Sulis Cutler for inspiration on this and other recipes.

ALMOND ROSE CHIA SHAKE

This vibrant shake is a natural rejuvenative and aphrodisiac.

Time: 20 minutes, with optional
overnight soak
Makes: 2 cups, serves 2

1 cup homemade or unsweetened plain almond milk (see directions page 39)
1 cup water
1 Tablespoon chia seeds
2 chopped Calimyrna figs (2 Tablespoons)
1 date (optional)
1/2 teaspoon vanilla extract
1/4 teaspoon rose water OR 1 heaping teaspoon organic red rose powder
OR 1 Tablespoon organic dried rose petals
A few strands of saffron (optional)

Boil the water and pour it over the chia seeds, figs, date, vanilla, and rose placed in a heatproof measuring cup. Soak for 15 minutes or more. To calm Vata most, soak overnight.

Put the soaked mix in a blender with the almond milk and the saffron. Blend until smooth. Serve warm or at room temperature, and drink.

Effects: calms Pitta and Vata, neutral for Kapha (the fewer nuts the better for Kapha)

Supports: energy, rejuvenation, muscles, reproductive system

Notes: I'm grateful to Ina Rucker http://bodyhealththerapy.com/ and Stephanie Rogers http://www.stephsbody-works.com/ for bringing this recipe down to earth in an accessible way.

VARIATION: For extra verve, you can add 1/4 teaspoon ashwagandha and/or shatavari to each serving, except in pregnancy.

Veggie teas are alkalizing and a great way to boost your electrolyte intake. Best yet, you get to eat the veggies after you make the tea! Enjoy four different veggie teas.

SWEET POTATO
GINGER TEA

Time: A leisurely 15 minutes
Makes: 3 (1-cup) servings

> 1 quart water
> 1 – 2 large cubed sweet potato, cubed
> 1 thin slice fresh ginger
> 1/2 teaspoon ground coriander
>   (optional for Vata, excellent for Pitta)

Bring the water to a boil in a medium stainless steel saucepan. Add the rest of the ingredients.
Simmer for 10 minutes and drain the cooking liquid into tea cups.
This hot vegetable tea is nice after a meal or any time you're looking for sweet without
the intensity of sugar. The sweet potatoes make a great breakfast mashed with a little ghee,
or you can add them to any dish you like.

Effects: *calms Vata & Pitta, neutral for Kapha (OK for Kapha in moderation, 1 – 2 times a week).*

This veggie tea supports: *digestion, plasma and ojas. It is grounding, rich in anti-oxidants and gives the immune system a boost. It is great for the lungs and skin.*

Comments: *An Asian tradition when preparing food, is to pray for the benefit of all sentient beings. You can chant any mantra or prayer you like, inwardly or outwardly. OM TARE TUTTARE TURE SVAHA is one to the Mother Buddha Green Tara who nourishes all beings.*

Note: *This naturally sweet tea is one of Amadea's personal favorites.*

GREEN DINO DETOX TEA

Time: A leisurely 15 minutes
Makes: 3 (1 cup) servings

  1 quart + 1/2 cup water
  1 bunch Lacinato (dinosaur) kale
  1 thin slice onion
  1 slice (2 inches thick) fresh lemon
  1-inch slice fresh ginger
  1/2 teaspoon ground tulsi

Bring the water to a boil. Tear the kale leaves off their stems and put into the water. Discard the stems or save for a soup stock. Add the rest of the ingredients and simmer until the greens are tender. Strain, using the steaming water as your drink. Use the greens in whatever dish you like. You could serve them with extra virgin olive oil and a splash of lemon or vinegar.

Effects: neutral Vata, strongly calms Pitta and Kapha.

This detox tea supports: plasma, red blood cells, muscle, bone, liver. Alkalizing.

Notes: The name for GREEN DINO DETOX TEA came from the Wagner-Hiester family. Thank you!
Our snarky first runner up was GREAT FOR YOUR BONES – NO BONE BROTH from veggie chef
and ASCE Lori Johnson of Cardamom Kitchen in Montana. http://cardamomkitchen.com/about/
Blessings all around!

EXTRA EASY VARIATION: Instead of the fresh lemon, ginger, and tulsi, use 1 bag of Organic India brand Tulsi lemon ginger tea. Follow directions above.

WINTER ROOT TEA

Time: 20 minutes
Makes: 3 (1cup) servings

   1 quart + 1/2 cup water
   2 medium (or 2 cups) raw parsnips (2 cups)
   1 small (or 1/2 cup) raw carrot (1/2 cup)
   1 large bay leaf
   1/2 teaspoon ground cardamom

Scrub the parsnips and carrot well and slice them into bite-sized pieces. Boil water in a stainless steel pot and add all the ingredients. Reduce heat to medium; simmer, covered for 10-15 minutes or until the veggies are tender, but not mushy. Drain the cooking liquid into mugs and enjoy. You can use the cooked veggies in a curry or in the PARSNIP SMOOTHIE below.

Effects: calms Vata & Pitta, neutral for Kapha (up to twice per week). This is a grounding food yet you are only drinking its essence. It is clear or vishada.

This tea supports: plasma and is grounding. Alkalizing.

Notes: Polarity therapist Cindy Wagner (http://www.breathe-in-wellbeing.com/) called this, "Mild, sweet, filling, grounding, earthy, soft. It reminded me of cooking parsnips with my "Mama" (grandmother) in Brooklyn, NY growing up."

VARIATION: If Kapha wanted to consume this daily, I would recommend adding a handful of chopped parsley to the brew to balance it.

VARIATION: PARSNIP SMOOTHIE: blend together 1/2 cup of the simmered tender vegetables and 1/2 cup of the cooking water. For a little extra zip, add 1/8 teaspoon of your favorite garam masala per cup of smoothie. This makes a pretty drink, anywhere from melon-colored to applesauce-hued, depending on your garam masala. Enjoy hot.

BEET QUEEN'S MAGIC TEA

Supportive to the liver and cheering to the mood, this unusual and robust beverage is created with the dusky pink water from simmering beets.

Time: 30 minutes
Makes: 4 cups

1 quart (4 cups) water
3 – 4 (or at least 1 cup) raw beets (at least 1 cup)
3 bags Organic India brand Tulsi Sweet Rose tea

Bring the water to a boil in a medium stainless steel saucepan and add the beets, whole or chopped, either is fine. Simmer covered on medium heat until the beets are tender, 15 – 20 minutes. Add the Tulsi Sweet Rose tea bags to the pot and simmer for another ten minutes or so. Strain the tea into a pitcher or individual cups and serve. Use the beets in a soup or as a colorful side dish.

Effects: balances all doshas.

This tea soothes: the spirit as well as supports plasma and red blood cells. Alkalizing.

Notes: Thanks to Michele Schulz, talented Ayurvedic chef and educator and Zoe Kelly Linkletter, innovative ASCE graduate for the inspiration and naming this one.

VARIATION: If you haven't got Tulsi Sweet Rose tea or you abhor stevia, which the tea contains, add 1 Tablespoon tulsi tea and 1/4 cup organic rose petals during the last ten minutes of simmering; strain.

TIP: You can make a ROSY BEET SMOOTHIE first and add an extra quart of cooking water to that recipe to cook the beets. When they are done, pour off a quart of the steaming beet water into a small saucepan and use it to make BEET QUEEN'S MAGIC TEA.

BASIC HOMEMADE ALMOND MILK

Ojas is built by nurturing all the tissues skillfully. This drink does this well!

Time: Overnight
Makes: 1 cup

8 – 10 raw almonds soaked in 2 cups of water with
1/2 teaspoon mineral salt
1 cup fresh water

Soak the almonds and salt overnight in 2 cups of water. Pinch their noses to peel them, and discard the soaking water. Blend the almonds with a fresh cup of water. If you have a Vitamix or other such wonder, this becomes beautiful and creamy and completely integrates the almonds into the liquid. If you have a blender, you'll have a few chunks of nuts to chew or strain out.

Effects: tridoshic. These are the best proportions to balance all doshas. If you add more almonds, as below, it will calm Vata well, yet can easily aggravate Pitta or Kapha.

This milk rejuvenates: all seven tissues and builds ojas.

Comments: In Ayurvedic medicine, this sattvic beverage acts as a nervine that revives mental as well as physical energy. The advantage of fresh homemade almond milk over prepared boxed or bottled almond milk is that it has substantially more vitality and prana. You can easily increase the proportions on this to make as much as you need. The fresher, the better. Peeling almonds increases their digestibility. The smoothness of the resulting milk soothes Vata and Pitta. To calm Vata even more, add a tiny pinch of salt.

EASY VARIATION: QUICK HOMEMADE ALMOND MILK: Boil the quart of water, pour over the almonds, let soak for 15 minutes. Proceed as above.

"Turmeric is the best medicine in Ayurveda. It cures the whole person."
- Dr. Vasant Lad

GOLDEN MILK AND SPICY HOT CHOCOLATE

GOLDEN MILK

Classic support for joints and immunity from Yogi Bhajan gets a fresh twist.

Time: 10 - 15 minutes
Serves: 2 (1 1/4 cup servings)

    1/4 teaspoon ground turmeric
    1 cup water
    2 cups milk of your choice
    1/2 Tablespoon grated fresh ginger
    1 teaspoon organic coconut oil or ghee
    3 – 5 black peppercorns
    1/2 teaspoon ground cinnamon
    Sweeten to taste with honey or stevia

In a small stainless steel pot over medium heat, stir the turmeric into the water and cook until it forms a nice "paste". This takes about 8 minutes. In a second medium stainless steel pot, whisk the rest of the ingredients and continue to wisk until it boils. As soon as it boils, immediately remove the milk mixture from the heat. Add the first pot to the second pot and whisk together. Strain the golden milk into mugs. If you'd like a little honey, now is the time to add it.

Effects: tridoshic.

This milk supports: all dhatus, especially plasma, red blood cells, muscle, fat, bone, ojas.

Note: Much thanks to Cynthia Bancale, our book designer, for this delicious beverage.

EASY FRESH VARIATION: Cynthia uses 1/2 Tablespoon of grated fresh turmeric in place of the ground turmeric and makes everything in one pot, omitting the step of making a turmeric paste. She uses homemade almond milk.

SPICY HOT CHOCOLATE (CHO-CO-LAH-TAY)

Nahautl Mexico meets ancient India!

Time: 10 – 15 minutes
Makes: 1 or more cups

1 cup water or milk of your choice per person, we prefer
    almond milk in this recipe
Add per cup:
1 1/2 Tablespoons organic cacao powder
1/4 teaspoon each: ground cinnamon and ground cardamom
1/8 teaspoon each: ground nutmeg and pippali
The tiniest pinch of mineral salt (omit if using dairy)
1/2 teaspoon shankhapushpi (optional)
1/2 - 1 teaspoon almond extract
Sweetener to taste

Bring the water or milk to steam in a pot. Add all ingredients except the sweetener. Stir well. Gently boil for 5 minutes. Take off heat; add sweetener. Whip the hot cacao mixture in the pot until frothy. (If you only use water, it doesn't froth.) Enjoy in a leisurely manner with a friend, up to once or twice per week.

Effects: neutral for Vata, increases Pitta, decreases/lightens/enlivens Kapha.

This beverage supports: nerves, digestion and circulation.

Comments: In Ayurveda, chocolate or cacao is considered to aggravate all doshas (Lad) by clogging the channels. Its usual travelling companions - an excess of milk and sugar - are part of the bad rap. The Aztecs made hot chocolate in water, not milk, and served it dark and bitter with honey. Bitter taste opens the srotas/ channels, as do cardamom, cinnamon and pippali. Cardamom antidotes theobromine, cacao's caffeine-like stimulant. Made like this, it has as close to a neutral effect on the doshas as possible.

SPICY NOT CHOCOLATE: in place of the cacao, use 1 heaping Tablespoon carob powder per cup for a surprisingly satisfying drink.

Effects: neutral for Vata, calms Pitta and Kapha.

Supports: digestion, nerves; cleanses fat.

HOT APPLE CIDER

This riff on a classic has half the fruit sugar of its original counterpart. It's great for chilly winter nights or ski days.

Time: 10 minutes
Makes: 2 (1 cup) servings

  1 cup apple juice or cider
  1 cup water
  1/2 teaspoon ground cinnamon or
      1 small cinnamon stick
  1/4 teaspoon ground nutmeg

Combine all ingredients in a small stainless steel pot. Simmer over medium high heat until steaming. Serve with the cinnamon stick or a thin slice of lemon or simply plain.

Effects: calms Pitta and Kapha, has a neutral effect on Vata.

This drink supports: hydration and plasma.

HEALING CHAI FOR TWO

This delightful classic brew from photographer Renee Lynn warms you up without wiring those doshas.

Time: 20 minutes
Makes: 4 cups

> 2 cups filtered water
> 2 Tablespoons freshly grated ginger root
> 3 cinnamon sticks
> 1 Tablespoon whole cloves
> 1 Tablespoon cardamom pods
> 1/4 teaspoon freshly grated nutmeg
> 2 cups organic milk of your choice
> 3 Tablespoons organic loose leaf decaffeinated black tea (Assam or Orange Pekoe)

Boil water, add the spices - ginger, cinnamon, cloves, cardamom, nutmeg - and simmer for ten minutes.

Add the milk and tea, bring it all to frothy hot, and remove from heat. Stir, cover and steep for five minutes. Strain and serve. Sweeten to taste.

Effects: calms Vata, neutral Kapha, increases Pitta (for neutral effect, reduce cloves to 1 teaspoon)

This chai supports: digestion, ojas and comradery.

Notes: The original basis of this recipe comes from Dr. Sharada Hall, DOM and Ayurvedic practitioner. http://www.bodhimed.com/dr-sharada-hall. *She uses almond milk.*

Spring: The Dance of the Doshas through the Seasons

Ayurveda as mood medicine

My friend and colleague Ralph Steele has used Ayurveda as a primary healing modality for years. He sees these drinks as medicine. A psychotherapist by profession and a Kapha by constitution, he responded to these recipes by first noticing how they affected his mind and mood. Given that he is also a meditation teacher, this is not surprising. It's all about awareness. The SWEET POTATO GINGER TEA, he found so calming, that he said he planned to use it for a "bedtime knockout". He called it "Deep Calm". The GREEN DINO DETOX TEA, a light veggie tea made with lots of dark leafy greens elicited a "refreshing sensation" in him. He likened it to being in Panchakarma, the powerful cleansing process of rejuvenation. His perspectives are classically Ayurvedic, in that the doshas can elicit mental and emotional responses, as well as physical ones.

The invitation that is Ayurveda

Within Ayurveda, we are all sacred beings with the divine spark in every cell. That divine spark can be communicated across space. The five elements of Ether, Air, Fire, Water, and Earth inform the metabolism of each and every part of our being. The psycho-biological energies known as Vata, Pitta, and Kapha are responsible for our balance – or imbalance – in health. We each come into this life with our own unique flavors, constitution or *prakruti*, meaning that each of us has different needs than anyone else. How we work with these needs and what comes to us in life influences our current condition or *vikruti*. In his generous foreword, Dr. Vasant Lad addresses these points most eloquently. Ayurveda takes into account every level of being, from the first spark of spirit to the last breath of dying.

My question is, how do we bridge the pristine blue print that is Ayurveda to the messy chaos of our own everyday lives? How do we create for ourselves some health and sanity? Ayurveda has been around for centuries, helping humans, animals and plants regain their equilibrium. Yet why would we turn to Ayurveda for help right now?

My friend Ralph uses Panchakarma to enhance his life and longevity. He was exposed to Agent Orange while serving in the US armed forces in Vietnam many decades ago. He is deeply aware that what he eats and drinks, and how he approaches life, can be the difference between fulfilled action or the peculiar blessing of bed sickness.

What you'll receive and discover

Renee and I originally began this all seasons easy healing drink book because so many of the people we know and work with need it: single people, people with families, working people, young people, older people, people with distressed guts, and people with little time or money to be able to cook. Some of them are vegetarians; some know Ayurveda; others do not. What can I offer them, or you? Exactly what we are sharing here: fast, simple, tasty, healing nourishment. It is based on time-honored principles of healing, appropriate for each individual.

Here we are in spring. Our job is to find our selves in this season, to discover our own balance of prakruti (constitution) and vikruti (current condition) within the myriad changes. We can regain some balance that makes sense to us. Among these changes are the vivid shifts of the seasons. As one young client wailed recently, "But I'm not ready for spring! I don't want to emerge." She still wanted the slow quiet darkness of winter. I could empathize. Yet like it or not, spring is upon us.

What moving into a new season means

Seasons also have doshas. The cool Kapha dampness of winter gives way to the warmth of spring. In spring, Kapha is still present, moist and precipitating, yet Pitta is coming forward, warming the earth and sky. In spring, in addition to noticing our current condition, we need to heed the demands of these two doshas, Kapha and Pitta. While in winter we were eating more earthy roots, now it's a time to lighten up and have more greens. If we're wise, we take it a little easier on oily, heavier foods. As in every season, we need to nourish the plasma, the liquid portion of our blood. We make sure to keep ourselves well hydrated.

Each season holds its own challenges. As you look at the following chart, you can see that each dosha swells to predominance, then subsides into a quieter state. In spring, as Kapha comes forward to be cleared, we may have more mucus, hay fever, spring colds. We're aware of the heaviness we may have gathered around us in winter and would like to shed. We're more inclined to let go of some of the heaviness on other levels as well and move into the light. Fortunately, Pitta is rising (it will peak in summer), helping us burn away some excess cold and damp. Yet fiery Pitta may show up in other ways as well, such as an impatience to have the changes done already, or perhaps as exasperation at ourselves for our slow ways. We need to be patient with our mistakes, past and present, as we create a new balance for ourselves in this season. Spring is a time of transition.

The Dance of the Doshas through the Seasons

Part of that healthy balance relates to how we care for our tissues. In the winter section, I described how in Ayurveda we work with seven dhatus, or essential tissues. The energy of each nourishes the others in a vast

The Dance of the Doshas through the Seasons

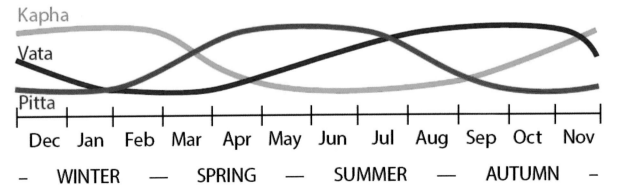

cellular network of metabolism. How we nourish our tissues in spring is a little different than how we did it in the cold of winter. Then we were working with Kapha at its peak, with chilly Vata close behind. Now as the earth is warmed by the sun, and Pitta sparks the metabolism of our cells, our tastes and choices change subtly. In spring, we're more interested in cleansing, as it is a great time to clear away old wastes. Kapha wants to be released and dissolved, and Pitta ready to enliven that process.

How the doshas watch over the dhatus, the seven essential tissues

If you were to go to an Ayurvedic educator like me to create a seasonal plan for yourself, I would consider not only the balance of your doshas, yet also the health of your dhatus. I would be keeping in mind some

subtle and not-so-subtle relationships. In Ayurveda, each tissue is supported and protected by a particular dosha. Hot-blooded rakta (blood cell tissue) is guarded by Pitta. Dry-as-a-bone asthi (joints and bone tissue) is watched over by Vata. Slow, steady, reliable Kapha supports all of the rest! (See THE DHATUS: ESSENTIAL TISSUES chart below.)

What does this mean, that Kapha guards a dhatu? If you want to cleanse a tissue like fat, meda dhatu, you'll need to do it in ways that are friendly to Kapha, as it is in charge of fat. Since in Ayurveda we work with opposites for healing, this means that the drinks we will use to cleanse fat will be warm, light, dry, enlivening or spicy ones. Yet you're a human who has some Pitta dosha in them, too. Remember we all have all three doshas, just in different proportions. If you use too much hot and dry

The Dhatus: Essential Tissues

Sanskrit	English	Guardian of this dhatu
Rasa	Plasma, liquid blood & lymph	Kapha
Rakta	Red blood cells	Pitta
Mamsa	Muscle	Kapha
Meda	Fat	Kapha
Asthi	Bone	Vata
Majja	Bone marrow, nerves & fascia	Kapha
Artava Shukra	Female reproductive system Male reproductive system	Kapha Kapha

and light, those hot red blood cells may get aggravated and spur a skin rash! In Ayurveda, it's all connected.

This spring recipe collection has specific actions to support your tissues. Each recipe offers a bit of cushion, something that appeals to every dosha, so that one dosha or dhatu does not get offended and give you more trouble than you want.

If you are working with diabetes, start with the vegetable-based recipes, rather than the fruit ones. Choose recipes with generous amounts of protein, such as hemp, pumpkin or sunflower seeds. If you'd like to try a fruit-based recipe, cut the fruit juice substantially with water. Look in the index for recipes specifically healing for diabetes. Recipes that support the adrenals, liver, or pancreas will also be helpful for you.

The delicate melodies of the tastes

Internationally respected Ayurvedic physician Dr. Vasant Lad discusses in his foreword how one creates Ayurvedic recipes. One needs to think a good amount about *rasa* (taste), *virya* (energy), and *vipak* (post-digestive effect). How will this drink taste? Will it warm someone up or cool them down? What are the long-term effects of eating this food regularly? These issues need to be considered, if you want to feel well and be well. If Pitta is rising and excess Kapha needs to be dissolved in spring time, what tastes do we need? More bitter and astringent flavors will calm and address these emerging changes. If sensitive Vata dosha is still with us in the midst of all this world turbulence, we cannot forget him or her as well.

We calm our Pitta and Kapha doshas with bitter and astringent dark leafy greens; they thrive on them. On the other hand, no matter what greens you pick for Vata, you're going to need to use them moderately. Warm them up, steam them, mix them with something creamy. Otherwise poor Vata will get all dry and goofy, and there's no shortage of that around these days. In the appendix on how to **Play with Dark Leafy Greens** you can find an entire chart from which to choose for your specific needs.

Understanding digestion and food combining

In Ayurveda, the digestive tract is the gateway to health. In order to assimilate the easy healing drinks you'll be making, you need to be able to digest them. Each recipe includes key digestive components to support good assimilation, including harmonizing spices or particular ways of preparing foods that make them easier to digest and absorb.

Ayurveda has particular ways of combining foods based on centuries of healing experience that are literally quite foreign to us non-East Indians. The frosty smoothies that have been a cornerstone for decades in holistic health diets, quietly appall many an East Indian practitioner. Depending on their temperament, they will either be too polite to tell you this, or they may beat you over the head with the Ayurvedic food combining practices. I'm here to politely say, if you can keep ice out of your meals, you'll assimilate the nourishment better. If you are willing to combine a ripe banana with some almond milk, seeds or a little fruit juice, rather than cow's milk or dairy, your gastrointestinal tract is likely to thank you with greater vitality. If you decide to not mix fruit with veggies in fresh juices, you are likely to have less gas. Okay. So much for secrets. There's more of this poetic wisdom in the recipes that follow.

What is not needed

You don't have to be perfect. Feel free to experiment with what's here. Anybody can use these recipes. You don't have to be a vegetarian or Ayurvedic to make or eat them. On the other hand, it's fine if you are. Many of my clients are not strict vegetarians. They are just here to get well, and appreciate plant-based healing. You can, too.

I do believe actions of love and non-violence matter. Understanding the concepts behind Ayurveda healing can definitely motivate you to change your life positively. A web of connection exists beyond that which we can conceptually understand, which can be directly experienced. Healing can come from direct connections experientially.

Reaching out in spring

As the flowers were just starting to break through the dry crust of southwestern, high mountain soil, I met with an old friend, Tim, who first encountered Ayurveda some 28 years ago. I asked him what Ayurveda means to him now. A quiet man with clear sparkling eyes, he said in his light, even-handed way, "I think Ayurveda really offers a lot to people, anything that gets people to look inside. It's a discipline that people can take with them their whole lives, and that's valuable." A Western herbalist and former college professor of Vata-Pitta constitution, Tim has used many healing methods over the years, including Western medicine. He keeps a lid on gluten, garlic, and peppers according to the Ayurvedic recommendations he's applied for years. Yet, the real message I hear from him today is more about spiritual renewal than about any particular way of eating or drinking.

"The center of nature is about giving. Ayurveda, nutrition, herbs and complementary alternative medicine all help me to give so much more. Why not emphasize the positive?" Tim takes joy in small actions of kindness like coming early to set up for the choir in which he sings. The generosity of nature and the possibility that others, too, can be generous is what he wants to emphasize now. "(Practicing) this been challenging in (the) cold of winter as I found myself drawing in. As springtime comes, I'll be out more." Being willing to go out, to share, to open to the colors of the season is his message.

In that spirit, we offer you these spring recipes.

Amadea Morningstar and Renee Lynn

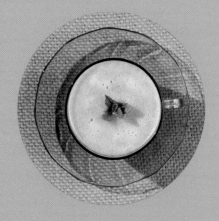

Spring is the time snow melts

from the mountain, and wastes

can most easily clear

from our bodies.

Spring Recipes

HOT OR COOL
STRAWBERRY SMOOTHIE

Beautiful, easy, and entirely scrumptious!

Time: 10 minutes
Makes: 2 (1 cup) servings

2 cups fresh organic strawberries
1 cup tangerine juice
1 tiny pinch ground cloves, 1/16 teaspoon or less

Wash and slice the tops off the strawberries. Put them in a stainless steel saucepan on medium heat with the juice and the cloves. Simmer 5 minutes until warm, blend, serve hot or cool, depending on your needs and the weather.

Effects: neutral for all three doshas taken in moderation. The tangerine juice could aggravate Pitta and Kapha if eaten daily. If you love the flavor of this smoothie and have more Pitta or Kapha to calm than Vata, try the variation below.

This smoothie supports: plasma, blood cells, immunity, ojas.

Notes: Depending on where you live, the toughest part of this recipe could be finding the ingredients. Feel free to use any dosha-balancing, healthy fruit juice you can obtain. For more thoughts about this recipe, sustainability, pesticides, and protecting honey bees, see https://amadeamorningstar.net/honeybees-nourishment-easy-healing/

VARIATION: In place of the tangerine juice, use 1 cup apple juice. Equally delicious.

Effects: Calms Pitta and Kapha, neutral for Vata taken occasionally.

*This refreshing recipe
is much more pleasing than
eating a grapefruit with a spoon!*

FRESH GRAPEFRUIT
SLIMMING ELIXIR

Time: 5 minutes
Makes: 1 1/2 cups

1 fresh ruby red grapefruit, segmented, with the seeds (optional)
   (= 2 cups)
1 very thin slice ginger, 1/4" or less
1/2 cup water
Juice of 1/2 lime or lemon
Sweetener (optional)

Blend the grapefruit. Add the rest of the ingredients and blend again. Enjoy on an empty stomach or at the beginning of a meal, not at the end.

Effects: calms Vata and Kapha, increases Pitta if taken daily. It is most effective for Kapha if taken first thing in the morning.

This drink supports: digestion, cleansing of fat and phlegm, and discourages Candida overgrowth.

Comments: If Vata is leading your pack of doshas, if you're feeling stagnant yet wired and anxious, this could be a good choice. It's excellent for the nervous overweight Vata eater. Taken in the morning, it liquefies and reduces Kapha dosha. Taken later in the day or after food, its sour taste and vipak could aggravate Kapha and Pitta. (Tirtha, 131)

Notes: With appreciation to Manon C. Pierme, www.manollasenbi.com, holistic health practitioner, private chef, and ASCE graduate, for her practical insights.

Sweet ruby red grapefruit is called for here, not sour white! Even so, some people may want to add sweetener to taste.

This flavorful drink is friendly and gently aphrodisiac.

LAVENDER ROSE LEMONADE

Time: 1 hour plus a few minutes (think ahead)

Makes: 2 cups

1 cup water
1 Tablespoon dried organic lavender flowers
1 teaspoon dried organic rose flowers
1 Tablespoon fresh lemon zest
1 more cup of water
2 Tablespoons coconut sugar or raw honey
3 Tablespoons fresh lemon juice

Bring one cup water to a boil in a stainless steel saucepan, pour it over the lavender, rose and lemon zest in a stainless steel or Pyrex bowl; stir. Cover and let sit one hour. Strain. Warm the second cup of water, take it off the heat and stir in the sweetener and lemon juice. Do not heat the honey! Pour the two mixtures together and enjoy.

Effects: calms Vata, neutral for Pitta and Kapha.

This drink supports: production of digestive juices (lemon, lime, lavender), plasma, blood, temperature modulation (lemon zest), nerves (rose and lavender).

Comments: Rose, lavender, and coconut sugar all balance the warming quality of the citrus well. Rose is also a gentle aphrodisiac.

Notes: Thanks to Western herbalist and ASCE Lynn Childson for her inspiration on this.

Organic Rose Petals or Lavender: Our recipe testers had challenges sourcing organic rose petals. For your own organic flowers early in spring: nurture or find an organic rose bush or a lavender plant. When it blooms in late spring or early summer, make an offering to it with a song, a pinch of cornmeal, whatever speaks to you. Cut flowers you want to gather into a basket or bowl (not all of them of course). Spread them on a cookie sheet and set in a dry place to dry. When they are dry, store them in a clean, dry, glass jar. The flowers will keep for a year.

PITTA-KAPHA VARIATION: Add 1 Tablespoon or more organic aloe vera juice per cup; use lime juice in place of lemon.

DELICIOUS ANTI-INFLAMMATORY VARIATION: Soak 1 Tablespoon chia seeds in 1 cup of the LAVENDER ROSE LEMONADE for 30 minutes or more. Then, stir in 1 Tablespoon of aloe vera juice and 1/2 teaspoon fresh grated ginger (thanks to Renee Lynn).

KEY LIME PITTA MINT COOLER

This tasty drink is packed with mineral-rich foods.

Time: about 20 minutes
Makes: at least 1 1/2 cups

> 1/4 cup raw sunflower seeds
> 1/3 – 1/2 cup well-packed fresh mint leaves
> 1/4 cup fresh lime juice
> 1/2 small ripe avocado (2 level Tablespoons)
> 1 cup coconut water
> 1 Tablespoon coconut sugar
> 1 teaspoon peeled and finely chopped or grated fresh ginger
> 1/2 teaspoon ground cardamom
> 1/16 teaspoon pippali

In a blender, grind the sunflower seeds as finely as possible. Chop the mint finely and blend or pulverize it to a paste with the ground sunflower seeds, lime juice, and avocado. Blend in the rest of the ingredients. Drink!

Effects: very calming to Pitta, calms Vata & Kapha.

This beverage supports: digestion, free flow of prana and energy.

Comments: Mint has the unusual quality of being able to normalize the flow of prana throughout the body. It can decongest blocked Vata and lift both emotional and mental tension. "It opens spaces and creates room for movement." (Pole, 226)

COOLING COCONUT GREEN DRINK

An easy, pleasant way to ingest spring greens!

Time: 10 - 15 minutes
Makes: 1 cup

    1/3 cup well-packed cilantro, finely chopped
    1 teaspoon peeled cut chopped fresh ginger
    1 Tablespoon fresh lime juice
    1 cup organic coconut water
    1 teaspoon coconut sugar (optional)
    1/2 cup or more dark leafy greens of your choice

In a blender, pre-pulse the cilantro, ginger and lime juice until they are as smooth as possible. Add the coconut water and coconut sugar; blend until smooth. Now it's time to play: blend in as much of your favorite greens as you like. (With a $20 blender, there are likely to be some chunks in this one, which you can strain out, if you want.) Enjoy!

Effects: very calming to Pitta, calms Kapha, neutral to Vata in moderation. Raw greens increase Vata, although the ginger, lime and the liquidity of the drink all make it less aggravating. Yogurt or coconut milk are other ways to calm Vata, see Variations below.

This drink supports: plasma, blood cells, muscles, immunity.

Notes: This magnesium-rich Pitta and Kapha-subduing drink is an improvisation on Mataji Desai's "Gujarati Fresh Coriander Chutney" from our Ayurvedic Cookbook.

VARIATION: Iza Bruen-Morningstar, one of our recipe testers, shares, "To cut the bitterness of the greens, it's helpful to add coconut milk or yogurt. As a result, the recipe may not need the lime juice or added coconut sugar. I used half a bunch of dino kale, an entire bunch of cilantro, only half a cup of coconut water and a quarter cup of plain yogurt. (The result) was slightly bitter, but definitely sweet enough. I love this drink!"

This simple, nourishing shake can be easily adapted in many ways.

THE VATA CLASSICO SHAKE *YEAR-ROUND*

Time: 5 minutes, plus 30 minutes soaking seeds
Makes: one cup

    1 Tablespoon flax seeds
    1/2 cup hot water for the soak
    1/2 cup fresh almond milk or plain, unsweetened ready-made organic almond milk
    1/2 ripe banana
    1/2 cup or more fresh berries (optional)
    1 thin slice fresh ginger, peeled and well chopped
    1/8 teaspoon ground cinnamon
    1/8 teaspoon nutmeg
    1/2 teaspoon raw honey or 1/2 packet or 1/2 teaspoon stevia (optional)

Soak the flax seeds and hot water together for 30 minutes or more. Grind the seeds in a blender or food processor. This step gives you extra protein, Omega 3's and a bit of mood-calming, as well as laxative action. Add the rest of the ingredients and blend the shake until smooth.

Effects: calms Vata, fine for Pitta or Kapha twice per week, as well tolerated.

This shake supports: elimination, plasma, blood, muscle, fat, bone, marrow, nerves, ojas, healthy pregnancy, and lactation.

Comments: This shake really helps a dry Vata digestive system move along. Pitta may find the flax seeds too moving. For Pitta and Kapha, you can substitute 1 Tablespoon of chia seeds, lighter, cooler, less laxative and even richer in Omega 3 fatty acids.

From an Ayurvedic food combining point of view, banana mixed with cow's milk or yogurt is considered quite hard to digest, despite its popularity on the American holistic health scene. This shake is one Ayurvedic answer to: "how can you use banana in a smoothie?" Feel free to use this recipe as a simple template with other fruits.

Notes: Thanks to acupuncturists Connie Fisher in Seattle and Alyiah Doughty in Santa Fe (http://fiveelementacupuncturist.com/) for their input on this recipe.

Here's a tasty way for Kapha to get liquid greens, with inspiration from Sri Lanka.

SAMBOL DRINK AND CAULIFLOWER SMOOTHIE

SAMBOL DRINK, KAPHA STYLE

Time: 10 – 15 minutes
Makes: 1 1/4 cups

    1/2 cup coconut water
    1 teaspoon lemon or lime juice
    2 Tablespoons finely chopped cilantro
    1/4 teaspoon paprika
    1/8 teaspoon pippali
    1/2 cup fresh carrot juice
    1/2 cup well-packed raw spinach or tender kale

Using a blender or food processor, blend the cilantro to a paste with a little of the coconut water. Add the rest of the ingredients; blend again. Enjoy at room temperature.

Effects: calms Kapha, neutral for Vata, increases Pitta (due to the warming spices).

This drink supports: alkalizing, cleansing the liver and blood. It is rich in beta-carotenes.

Notes: The original inspiration for this was the "Sri Lankan Coconut Sambol" sauce in At Home with Madhur Jaffrey, a great cookbook. And thanks to Vaastu artist Marguerite Wilson for her practical wisdom (http://artquilts.co/vaastu-architecture/).

VATA VARIATION: Skip the lemon or lime juice and add 3 – 4 Tablespoons plain yogurt instead. In Ayurveda, friendly food combinations are an essential part of easy digestion. Lemon and yogurt are considered to be a difficult combination together, so instead use one or the other here. For more about food combining, see Usha & Vasant Lad, *Ayurvedic Cooking for Self-Healing*.

KAPHA VARIATION: For even more greens for Kapha and a diuretic action, blend in 1 Tablespoon finely chopped parsley.

CAULIFLOWER SMOOTHIE *YEAR-ROUND*

This lovely lemon-colored drink makes a satisfying lunch, dinner, or snack.

Time: 30 minutes
Makes: 2 1/2 cups, serves 3

  1 small cauliflower
  1 – 2 Tablespoons olive oil
  1/2 teaspoon ajwan seeds
  1 Tablespoon fresh ginger, peeled and finely chopped
  3 green onions, finely chopped
  1/4 teaspoon turmeric
  1/4 teaspoon mineral salt
  1/8 – 1/4 teaspoon Serrano chili, finely chopped (optional, less for Pitta)
  2 cups water

Wash and break up the cauliflower into florets; place in a bowl of water while you prep the rest of the smoothie. Peel and finely chop the ginger. (An easy way to do this is scrape off the peel with a spoon.) Finely chop the green onions and chili; set aside.

In a heavy, flat-bottomed stainless steel skillet, warm the oil over medium heat, add ajwan; stir until aromatic. Stir in the ginger and green onion for a minute then the turmeric. Scoop up the cauliflower from the water with your hands and drop it into the pot. (Jaffrey, *Vegetarian India*, 78) Add salt and the chili, stir, cover. Reduce heat to low, cook about ten minutes or the cauliflower until is tender enough to break apart with a fork. Add the water, turn up the heat to medium, cover, simmer for five minutes or until gently bubbling. Put the hot veggie mixture in a deeper pot or bowl to blend it smooth with a hand held immersion blender.

Effects: calms Kapha and Vata, neutral Pitta. Add 1/4 cup or more plain yogurt for Vata for extra calcium and protein.

This warm smoothie supports: digestion, respiratory system, nerves. It is a diuretic.

Comments: A cancer preventive, cauliflower is considered easier to digest and more sattvic than other cabbage family members. It combines well with dairy (Tirtha, 136).

ARTICHOKE BAY TEA *YEAR-ROUND*

A mild, liver-soothing drink to use after times of excess.

Time: 45 – 50 minutes or the time it takes to simmer an artichoke

Makes: 2 – 4 cups

2 quarts of water
2 or more organic artichokes
1 large bay leaf

In a large pot, bring the water to a boil. Add the artichokes and bay leaf. Simmer on medium heat for 40 – 50 minutes, or until a test leaf is tender and pulls out easily, just like you would do for a pineapple. Remove the artichokes to be eaten. Save the cooking water for this veggie tea recipe. It can be drunk hot or at room temperature.

Effects: balances all doshas.

This veggie tea supports: digestion, elimination, plasma, blood cells (hemostatic), female reproductive system. It is a diuretic.

Comments: Artichoke being a member of the milk thistle family, this veggie tea is most excellent for the liver. This sweet and astringent vegetable has a warm virya (energy) and a sweet vipak (post-digestive effect). It is helpful in excessive menstruation, as is asparagus (Tirtha, 134). The bay leaf brings out the liver cleansing, channel-clearing qualities of the artichoke and promotes digestion and assimilation (Lad & Frawley, 56-57). This veggie tea is a useful antidote when one has engaged in excessive damp, sticky food, including dairy, or meat (Tirtha, 156).

THE TULSI QUEEN TEA

This extraordinarily simple tea has got to be tried.

Time: 10 - 15 minutes
Makes: 2 cups

2 1/2 cups water
2 cups well-packed organic arugula leaves
1 Tablespoon dry tulsi powder, or 2 Tulsi tea bags
Raw local honey or sweetener of your choice (optional)

In a medium stainless steel pot, bring the water to a boil. Add the arugula and tulsi, and turn off the heat. Cover and steep for 5 – 10 minutes; strain. The tea can be drunk hot or at room temperature. If you wish to plus to carry the healing properties deeper into the tissues, sweeten to taste with raw honey to enhance the decongesting properties of tulsi (Pole, 281).

Effects: calms Kapha and Vata, increases Pitta if taken daily.

This veggie tea supports: digestion, plasma, liver, heart, respiratory tract.

Comments: Other sweeteners can be used, yet they do not have the specific decongesting action of raw honey.

Notes: Our testers adored this very easy arugula tulsi tea. It fits the bill in spring or fall, when arugula is abundant. The TULSI QUEEN owes its name to tester Stephanie Rogers of Fire Island, New York. https://www.stephsbodyworks.com/ She has also created variations on this recipe with fresh dandelion, stinging nettle, and a bit of mint.

ASPARAGUS SAFFRON MILK TEA *YEAR-ROUND*

This appealing, easy drink is a different kind of rejuvenative golden milk!

Time: 15 minutes
Makes: 2 cups, serves two

    1/2 cup plain unsweetened organic almond milk or organic cow's milk
    Pinch of saffron (optional)
    2 1/2 cups water
    1 bunch organic asparagus (1 pound)

Warm the milk in a medium pot. Remove from heat and add the saffron if you are using it. Let steep 10 minutes.

In a wide, flat skillet with deep sides, bring the water to a boil. Wash the asparagus and break off the tougher bottoms. (If you have a juicer, the tough stems can be used to make REJUVENATIVE VEGGIE JUICE). Prepare the asparagus however you want to eat it: whole or in pieces. Add the asparagus to the water. Simmer, covered, until tender, about 5 minutes. Reserve it to be eaten in whatever dish you like. Save the cooking water; stir it into the pot with the milk-saffron mix. Serve hot or at room temperature.

Effects: balances all doshas. It is a surprisingly relieving, calming beverage.

This veggie tea supports: digestion, elimination, plasma, heart, bone, and nerves. It energizes both female and male reproductive systems, and it builds ojas. It is useful in relieving edema.

Comments: Asparagus and saffron are both rejuvenative for the reproductive tract; milk is building (Tirtha, 135). While asparagus tea alone is fine in pregnancy, saffron is contraindicated as it stimulates the circulation of blood within the uterus (Pole, 259).

Notes: Some of our recipe testers were keenly aware of financial sustainability; this is a pricey drink. One advantage: you can enjoy the asparagus in whatever dish you like.

CLEANSING VARIATION: in place of milk, use 1 – 2 Tablespoons organic aloe vera juice, or to taste. Do not warm the aloe vera; simply stir the saffron into it; let it rest the 10 minutes. Aloe vera carries the cleansing qualities of this tea to every dhatu.

SARAH'S RASA TEA YEAR-ROUND

Time: 35 minutes or less
Makes: 3 cups

1 quart of water
2 Tablespoons red raspberry leaves
1 Tablespoon each: fenugreek seeds
fennel seeds
dried peppermint
1 teaspoon licorice root *
1 thin slice of fresh ginger (optional)
1/2 teaspoon rose hips
3 – 4 cardamom pods
1 Tablespoon flax seeds per cup (optional)

In a medium stainless steel saucepan, bring the water to a boil. Turn the heat to low, and add all the ingredients, except the flax seeds. Cover and simmer over low heat for 10 minutes, or turn off heat and steep for 30 minutes or more.

Before serving, strain the tea. If you like, stir the Omega3-rich, ojas-enhancing flax seeds into each cup.

If the weather is warm, feel free to store the tea in the fridge, and pour a cup at a time, letting it head toward room temperature before drinking. Or, if you're in a hurry, pour one-half cup in a tea cup and top it off with hot water.

Effects: balances all doshas, tridoshic, especially nourishing for post-natal mothers.

Supports: digestion, plasma, blood cells, female reproductive health, lactation.

*Caution: if you have high blood pressure or edema, skip the licorice or use only 1/4 teaspoon.

This cleansing tea is made of earthy, dried roots.

HEALING ROOTS TEA   *YEAR-ROUND*

Time: 15 - 20 minutes
Makes: 2 - 3 cups

1 quart water
1/4 cup sarsaparilla root
2 Tablespoons raw dandelion root (not roasted)
1 Tablespoon red root
1 Tablespoon burdock root

For this decoction, bring the water to a boil in a medium stainless steel pot. Add all the herbs and simmer on medium low for 10 - 15 minutes. Strain, offer the roots up to the compost. Serve. If you like, sweeten to taste with raw, local honey or sweetener of choice.

Effects: calms all doshas in moderation, especially Pitta and Vata.

Supports: digestion, plasma, blood, liver, kidneys, reproductive tissue, ojas.

Comments: Sarsaparilla cleanses the blood and liver and is considered to purify emotions as well. It is excellent for weak digestion (Tierra & Cantin, 126 – 127). It increases agni and dispels Vata from the intestines (Lad & Frawley, 145). It has the unusual property of binding bacterial endotoxins in the gastrointestinal tract, making them unabsorbable. This significantly reduces stress on the liver, colon, and skin. https://www.drugs.com/npp/sarsaparilla.html Useful in skin rashes and boils, it reduces infection, and it is antiviral. A rejuvenative, it builds ojas. Dr. David Frawley considers it one of the best diuretics (Frawley, 185). Dandelion, red root, and burdock are excellent blood cleansers, lymphatics and liver supports in their own right. If you do not wish to use a phytoestrogen, which sarsaparilla is, feel free to use the rest of this adept, hard-working crew of roots. (Additional resources: Moore, Wood).

TRUE TONING TEA (TTT!) *YEAR-ROUND*

Very simple. Earthy, woody, kind, comforting.

Time: Overnight
Makes: 2 cups

2 cups water
1 teaspoon true Soloman's Seal root (*Polygonatum multiflorum*)

In a clean glass Mason jar, add the water and true Solomon's Seal root. Shake a bit, doing mantras if you like. Place on a cool shelf and let sit overnight. The root expands in a pretty way and mostly drops to the bottom. Strain the next morning. Drink 1 – 2 cups/day. (Up to 3 cups/day can be consumed.) Once you've strained it, if you want to warm it up, feel free to do so.

Effects: tridoshic. In excess, its cool, moist qualities might increase Kapha.

This tea supports: digestion, mucous membranes, lungs and throat, muscles, ligaments, tendons, joints, bones, nerves, female and male reproductive tracts.

Comments: With the arrival of spring, one can be tempted to overdo activities. This simple tea has been used for centuries to tonify ligaments and tendons. Consider taking it daily for six weeks or more. It supports muscles and bones, as well as ligaments and tendons, after stress and in recovery after surgery. It is useful in both tightening loose ligaments, and loosening tight ones. It can be taken after chiropractic adjustments to stabilize changes.

A cooling and moistening demulcent, it can be drunk to calm an inflamed gut, vagina, or uterine tract; Candidiasis; or ruffled nerves. It is a mild diuretic (Wood, 397 – 406, also www.solomonsseal.net).

Notes: I am grateful to Lynn Childson, medicinal herbalist, ASCE graduate and manager of Herbs Etc. in Santa Fe, New Mexico for introducing me to this tasty and effective healer. Easiest to find in an herb store, Solomon's Seal can be expensive. To keep your expenditure under $5, start with one tablespoon to test.

SIMPLE COMFORT TEA *YEAR-ROUND*

Time: 15 minutes
Makes: 3 cups

1 quart water
6 inches of fresh lemongrass
1/4 cup fresh lemon balm leaves

Boil the water in a medium stainless steel pot. Wash the lemongrass and macerate it on a cutting board with a pestle or heavy stone. Simmer on low in the water for ten minutes, add the lemon balm, cover and steep five more minutes. Strain and serve.

Effects: tridoshic. In excess, theoretically it could increase Vata, yet this has not been my experience.

This tea supports: plasma, nerves, female and male reproductive tracts, immunity, ojas. It is a mild diuretic.

Comments: SIMPLE COMFORT TEA *tastes great and has a wide range of benefits. It lifts spirits, including in depression. It is anti-viral, and excellent for warding off a flu or infection before it can take hold. I make this by the thermos when I need it.*

VARIATION: You can also use dried lemongrass and lemon balm to make this tea. Cover and steep 10 – 15 minutes, or until it smells inviting to you.

A VERY QUICK VARIATION, if you have the following: in 1 quart boiled water, stir in 1 – 2 drops food grade essential oil of lemongrass (I choose DoTerra) and 100 drops lemon balm tincture (4 dropperfuls). Same effects and supports as above.

Ayurveda & Fresh Vegetable Juices

FRESH VEGETABLE JUICES: are not conventionally used in Ayurvedic medicine, although fresh macerated ginger juice and fresh plants have been respected as medicinal substances for centuries. Mechanical juicers did not exist, fresh raw fluids may have been seen as carriers for microbes, and in general, concentrated raw vegetables could quickly imbalance Vata. All this said, in these times, with easy access to safe, efficient juicers, I find that in warm weather, for Pitta and Kapha, fresh vegetable juices can have a strong place and purpose. They are alkalizing, vitamin and mineral rich, and can be easily digested, especially if they include digestives like ginger, fresh fennel, or mint.

Please note that in Ayurveda, vegetables and fruits are not usually combined in a dish for best ease of digestion, especially raw. We've worked to honor this in the following veggie juices. Lemon or lime can be added to vegetable juices as well tolerated.

I do not recommend large amounts of cold raw juice for Vata, particularly ones containing raw greens. Yet, a drink like the RAKTA-REVIVING VEGGIE JUICE that follows, with carrot and beet, gently warmed, is something I will definitely recommend when needed. The next five recipes all require a juicer.

RAKTA-REVIVING VEGGIE JUICE

This vibrant juice can be surprisingly sweet.

Time: 10 minutes
Makes: 1 1/2 cups, serves 2

3 - 4 medium carrots
1 small beet (1 cup)
1/2 cup well-packed fresh mint leaves

Juice together all the ingredients, alternating the carrots and beets with the mint leaves.

Effects: calms all doshas in moderation.

This juice supports: plasma, red blood cells, muscle, energy. It is alkalizing.

Comments: Beet builds blood and is warming. Mint dispels excess Vata, promotes healthy prana vayu (Pole, 226) and calms the heat of the beet.

Notes: Large carrots are often sweeter than small ones.

LIVER CLEANSE VEGGIE JUICE

Time: 10 minutes
Makes: 1 cup, 2 servings

3 large organic carrots
1 cup fresh organic dandelion leaves
1 inch fresh turmeric root
1/8 inch-thin slice fresh ginger
1 Tablespoon lime juice

With a juicer, juice all the ingredients, alternating easy-to-juice veggies like carrots with the more-challenging-to-juice greens. Enjoy on an empty stomach or before a meal.

Effects: calms Kapha, neutral Pitta, aggravates Vata.

This juice supports: cleansing of the liver and fat tissue, mucous membranes, plasma, immunity.

TUMMY SOOTHING VEGGIE JUICE

This vivid purple juice has an interestingly survivable flavor, and a beautiful color!

Time: 10 minutes
Makes: 1 1/4 cups juice plus 1 cup foam, serves 2 - 3

  1 small head red cabbage (4 cups)
  1 cup fresh cilantro, stems are fine
  1/4 organic lime with peel or 1 Tablespoon lime juice

Into a juicer, feed wedges of the cabbage, chopped cilantro and lime into a juicer. Enjoy the juice on an empty stomach, or before a meal.

Effects: calms Kapha and Pitta, increases Vata.

This juice supports: healthy stomach, digestive lining, muscles, immunity.

Comments: It seems counterintuitive to feature raw cabbage juice in an Ayurvedic cookbook, as it is the epitome of how to aggravate Vata! Yet there has been interest in the healing power of cabbage since research at Stanford University in 1949 (https://www.ncbi.nlm.nih.gov/pmc/articles/PMC1643665/) showed significant healing resulted for subjects with peptic ulcers. Cabbage is the most concentrated plant form of L-glutamine; red cabbage is particularly rich in phytonutrients. More recent research indicates that this amino acid speeds healing of stomach ulcers and IBS. http://news.harvard.edu/gazette/story/2009/05/glutamine-supplements-show-promise-in-treating-stomach-ulcers/ L-glutamine also supplies energy to the endothelial cells of blood vessels, and helps regulate their nitric oxide synthesis. This enhances blood flow.

Notes: While it is hard for me to imagine recommending it to someone with IBS or an otherwise sensitive colon, I was surprised how tolerable this particular drink was!

Contraindications: Made from a cruciferous vegetable, cabbage juice would not be appropriate for daily use in hypothyroid conditions. Clearly this would also not be recommended in most cases for excess Vata.

VERY VERDANT VEGGIE JUICE

Time: 10 minutes
Makes: 1 – 1 1/4 cup

1 head Romaine lettuce
1 cup well-packed fresh parsley
1 organic lemon with peel
1/2-inch slice fresh ginger
2 Tablespoons organic aloe vera juice

With a juicer, juice all the ingredients, adding the bottled aloe vera juice last.

Effects: calms Kapha and Pitta strongly, increases Vata.

This juice supports: plasma, reducing fat, calm nerves, diuretic, anti-inflammatory.

Notes: If you juice a fresh medium aloe vera stalk instead of using pre-made bottled aloe vera juice, for best results, put the stalk through the juicer first, before any of the other vegetables.

REJUVENATING VEGGIE JUICE

Time: 10 – 15 minutes
Makes: 2 1/2 cups

2 cups of asparagus, the tough part of the stem
4 cups fresh fennel bulb, the vegetable
2 -3 medium carrots

In a juicer, alternate the vegetables as you feed them into the machine.

Effects: calms Pitta and Kapha, mildly increases Vata (raw veggies).

This juice supports: plasma, female and male reproductive systems, ojas.

Notes: For the raw juice, use the bottom third of the asparagus that might normally be discarded. The rest of the asparagus, also tridoshic, can be used in any dish you like. A fennel bulb juices more easily than a stalk. (These vegetables in cooked form calm Vata.)

SPEEDY PACHAK LASSI   *YEAR-ROUND*

*"Pachak" is Sanskrit for digestion or digestive. This healing yogurt drink is
traditionally taken after meals to enhance digestion and absorption.
Try it – it's quick and easy to make in a mug.*

Time: 5 minutes
Serves: one

Ingredients	Thick Style, to serve one fast-moving VATA	Thick Style, to serve one determined PITTA	Very Thin Style, to serve one engaged KAPHA
Water	1/2 cup	1/2 cup	3/4 cup
Plain unsweetened yogurt	1/2 cup	1/2 cup	1 teaspoon to 1 Tablespoon
Ground cumin	1/2 teaspoon	1/2 teaspoon	1/2 teaspoon
Ground cardamom		1/2 teaspoon	
Ground dry ginger			1/4 teaspoon
Ground black pepper or pippali			1/4 teaspoon

Boil the water. As it heats, put the rest of the ingredients into a mug. Let the hot water rest for a minute before adding it to the live, active culture of friendly probiotics in the yogurt. Stir and serve. Or you can blend it, to enhance digestive fire.

Effects: calms all doshas with the appropriate versions. For Pitta, you can try 1 teaspoon of ground coriander in place of the cumin and cardamom.

This drink supports: digestive system, elimination, bone, nerves, healthy pregnancy, and lactation.

Comments: This warm drink enhances calcium intake (especially the Kapha version) and fills in the cracks if you're still a bit hungry at the end of a meal.

YOGURT VARIATIONS: Try this with sheep or goat yogurt or coconut milk yogurt. If you're substituting dense coconut yogurt, use half or less the amounts listed.

Summer: The Rhythm of Agni through the Seasons

Welcome home

Margie is 87. An attractive woman with snow white hair, for forty years she lived in the moist woods of the Pacific Northwest in a cabin she helped to build herself. Ferns and wild flowers grew in abundance. There wasn't much summer there. Two summers ago, she moved to the mountains of New Mexico with its vast skies and arid climate, a place she's always loved. This story is close to home for me, literally and figuratively. I (Amadea) am one of Margie's six children, and she lives next door to us now.

It happens to be a different kind of summer for us this year. Usually if our garden is fortunate enough to flourish, it does so on the cool edges of the season, in spring and fall. By mid-summer most years, almost everything would be crisped out in the dry Southwestern heat, 7,000 feet notwithstanding. This year, our place is blooming; it's beautiful and productive. Margie's sharp eyes and keen awareness have the time to take in far more detail than either my fast-moving husband Gord or me. She rejoices in the purple-flowered, silver-leaf nightshade that lines the front walkway, a weed that blossomed anonymously for decades under our watch. Cholla, prickly pear, and nicotiana all receive her appreciation. And respond. Bright cultivars and herbs cluster in wide swathes of color in pots around her door, a burgeoning harvest.

A clear and outspoken Pitta by constitution, Margie is not a particular fan of Ayurveda. Herbal teas and oil massages do not appeal to her. She's not a vegetarian. She does use certain Ayurvedic herbal formulas to strengthen her system, along with daily walks up the long driveway to pick up her mail and the newspaper.

She has a strong sense of the seasons and the healing power of color. This past August, I asked her what it was like to be in New Mexico now. She replied, "Well, there's a lot more sunshine. Yet, I'm very glad it has cooled off with the rain. You look forward to summer so much, then it's hot." Keenly aware of climate change, she pointed out, "it set records in Portland, Oregon last week: 107 degrees." Her summary? "At this time of year, I'm looking forward to cooler weather."

We are in a time when the days are longest; light is greatest. Many vibrant fruits and vegetables are peaking. How to enjoy summer to its utmost? Depending on the balance of our doshas and our digestive fire, the answers will be a little different for each of us.

What we've covered so far

In the opening intro for winter, we considered how food nourishes the dhatus/essential tissues. We introduced the gunas, the alphabet of Ayurvedic self-care: how to use attributes like light and heavy, cool and hot in practical healing (see Appendix 1 and 2). In the spring section, we saw how the doshas dance through the seasons by rising and falling, and came to understand that they're not a steady state! We explored how each dosha guards the health of specific tissues. Now, we will investigate how agni shifts and changes over the course of a year. Ayurveda engages change in a pro-active manner, and here we'll see how these changes relate to the summer season.

Moving into summer

In early summer, we begin with a clear sense that we need to keep cool in the face of Pitta heat. This can be pretty straightforward: drinking more cooling (not icy) fluids, using soothing mists, having a determination to not overwork (if at all possible), resting in shady places when we can, walking and playing in the cool of the day. We take in enough hydration in the face of increased perspiration. The theme is all about keeping cool, while balancing our own, unique blend of the doshas. Since sweet, bitter, and astringent tastes calm Pitta best, it is easy to gravitate toward these. Consider the recipes that follow: CUCUMBER DELIGHT, POMEGRANATE CHIA SMOOTHIE, HIBISCUS SUN COOLER, and CUCUMBER AGUA FRESCA. More fresh, ripe, sweet fruits are available to enjoy in the summer and can be used in easy-to-make drinks like THE TROPICANA, PEACH HEMP SHAKE or WATERMELON SPICE. Cooling coconut is here to help us in its myriad forms; we vault on to the bandwagon with our SPORTS SOLUTION isotonic fluid. Pitta-calming, bitter and astringent foods take the form of soothing mint, fresh cilantro, lettuce, Asian greens, and raw spinach. We continue to use digestive spices in foods and drinks to support our ability to assimilate nutrients. These spices tend to be milder ones, used in smaller proportions, as we find in the MONSOON CHAI.

With regard to the temperature of summer fluids, Ayurveda takes it easy on extremes. Iced drinks are passed up as they can dilute hydrochloric acid and repress production of digestive enzymes (Western research on the digestive system substantiates this ancient view). Yet, we also take it easy on hot water at this point in the year because it can bring up Pitta, as many menopausal women discover. Pungent, sharply-spiced foods are used in far smaller quantities than in a cooler season. The fewer onions, garlic and chili we consume, the calmer our Pitta is likely to be. It's recommended to take it easy on the hot sun, enjoying nature on the cooler edges of the day. We address our individual conditions while balancing the Pitta of the season.

If we have more Pitta or Kapha in our make-up, we can eat more raw foods in summer, including a salad at lunch when agni is strongest (FYI: Ayurveda considers many raw foods heavy and more difficult to digest. This is particularly true for some of us Vata people, yet not always true for everyone). If we are working with Vata conditions, we trust ourselves and continue to eat more cooked rather than raw foods, even in warm weather. Our digestive systems can be relied upon to give us the feedback we need, that is, if we're willing to listen to them. If our stomach is rumbly-grumbly with salad, we listen. If it sings with interest, we take that in, too.

The unexpected rhythms of agni

While many of us approach summer with enthusiasm, it's actually one of the trickier of seasons to navigate in its duration. At certain points during the summer, we can feel flat-out exhausted. What's going on? Are we just working too much? – Or, are we lucky ducks, playing – too hard? Part of the issue is excess Pitta, which can produce summer fatigue. Agni is the other factor.

"Agni is the creative flame of transformation behind all life, as well as the acidic substance that breaks down food and stimulates digestion," herbalist Candis Cantin Packard puts it eloquently (Packard, 55). When agni, our digestive fire, is balanced and vital, our health is good; digestion, absorption and elimination are smooth; brain fog is non-existent; our senses and consciousness are clear. Our appetite is good. We're basically happy. Given the current stresses of life on the planet, such a state of balanced agni, *sama agni*, sounds like some kind of a fairy tale. Yet, this description reminds us that this fire is essential to our well-being and can be part of the solution to some of our difficulties. With healthy, balanced agni, we can take in what we need to nourish ourselves and burn up many toxins before they create problems. Without agni, toxic undigested waste in the form of ama can and does build, ferment, and percolate into our tissues. With low agni, we can feel sluggish,

foggy, stagnant, bloated. As a result, our appetite is low and elimination can be slow.

Agni has many of the same gunas/attributes as Pitta dosha. Both are hot, sharp, light, subtle, mobile, and penetrating. Agni is a strong, positive and transforming force. In its daily rhythm, agni peaks in mid-day, the hours during which Pitta is highest. Yet, from a seasonal perspective, there are some important distinctions to make between agni and Pitta. People with a predominance of Pitta **dosha** do tend to have strong agni. In general, agni is also highest during the Pitta time of **day**. Yet, in the Pitta **season** of summer, our agni tends to dip. How can this be? A gaggle of conditions converges to create this picture.

Appetite is an indicator of agni; the better it is, the stronger our digestive fire is, in most cases. Agni is actually strongest in winter as it gets pushed from the periphery of the cells into the GI tract. As humans, we tend to have the strongest appetite and the greatest ability to digest food in cool weather. We eat more.

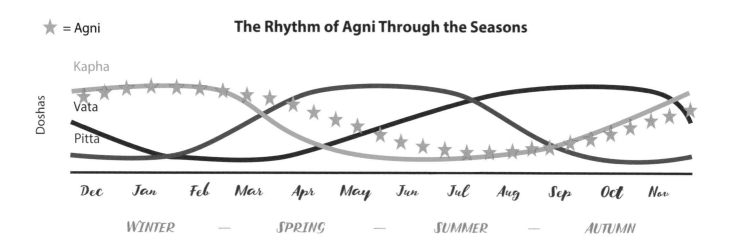

★ = Agni

The Rhythm of Agni Through the Seasons

Kapha

Vata

Pitta

Doshas

Dec   Jan   Feb   Mar   Apr   May   Jun   Jul   Aug   Sep   Oct   Nov

WINTER   —   SPRING   —   SUMMER   —   AUTUMN

Agni also remains present in spring to fire our metabolism and cleanse excess waste (See chart "The Rhythm of Agni through the Seasons"). Yet, in the heat of summer, both our strength and agni decline. (Nagral, 47 – 48; Lad, vol. 3, 79). We need to keep cool. We do this by sweating and drinking more fluids. Early in the summer, this dual formula works well to calm Pitta and ward off dehydration. Yet, the longer these two conditions persist through a long summer: 1) drinking excess fluids and 2) perspiring to lower body temperature, the more agni gets diminished. Our appetite drops and summer fatigue sets in, with excess Pitta.

The effects of summer rains and how to handle them

At this point of flat-out exhaustion and increased Pitta, if we are fortunate, the rains come, hopefully in the right quantity – not too much, nor too little. The rains do indeed calm Pitta dosha. Yet, they have a different effect on Vata and Kapha. With the monsoon, agni drops further and becomes dull. This agni is *manda agni*, the kind of digestive fire we usually associate with Kapha dosha. Vata accumulates under the surface of the season, causing a thready kind of instability. All three doshas can become rather uneasy with one another. So, how do we respond? How do we eat for this season? How can we positively harmonize all three doshas? Here are some suggestions:

With lower agni, we eat more lightly.

With lower agni, we drink smaller amounts of fluids. Slow down with that sipping!

We can favor clear beverages as they promote agni more than opaque, creamy ones.

We take it easier on cold, heavy, wet drinks, especially when it is raining. "Wait!", you might say. "This is summer. It's all about cold, wet drinks." Up to a point, yes. Yet, if you are feeling sluggish, not thirsty, and are staring out the window at the monsoon, conditions have changed. East Indians know this, yet we in the West are not always so wise.

It may be time to pull out the classic Ayurvedic digestive support of a thin slice of fresh ginger root with a squeeze of lime juice and a pinch of mineral salt sprinkled on top. This can be nibbled before meals, as needed, to ignite digestive fire. While sweet, bitter and astringent tastes soothe Pitta, it is the sour, pungent and salty flavors that build agni.

Using bitter taste judiciously can be win-win if Pitta is high, yet agni is diminished. A small amount of a bitter taste prior to a meal, whether it be aloe vera juice, gentian or Swedish bitters, can revive dulled agni and calm Pitta and Kapha. If Vata is in excess, this solution is less likely to be successful.

If we're wise, we'll drink less fluids in a late summer with rain; and these fluids can be spiced a bit more vividly to encourage agni. Light foods, not heavy ones, increase agni. Warm foods, not cold ones, encourage it. Sky gazing and a clear view, can improve agni. Agni is light and clear; do not impede it.

More ways to build agni

Some intriguing strategies from respected Ayurvedic physician Dr. Vasant Lad for building agni in summer include:

1. When tired and hungry, take a short nap – up to ten minutes – just before a meal. Before you lie down, sip a half cup of warm water, then lie down on your left side. This helps to kindle agni. When you get up ten minutes later, if you're really hungry, this is true hunger and you'll be ready to eat. If the hunger is emotional in origin (not true hunger), he suggests that it will disappear after the nap!

2. Consider a different condition: being energetic and hungry. In this case, don't lie down as it might only exasperate you. Take a short walk before the meal. Walking also encourages agni (Lad, vol. 3, 135).

Summer recommendations are for now these clear, light, cool, wise choices. Remember that soon autumn will be upon us. The need to calm Vata will then have us making warm, creamy drinks and soups again. Yet if you're willing right now, lighten up and let your agni and energy build.

With best wishes,

Amadea Morningstar and Renee Lynn

The key to summer wellness

is to keep cool, yet nurture

healthy digestive fire.

Summer Recipes

WATERMELON SPICE

This super simple recipe clears heat quickly.

Time: 5 minutes
Makes: 1 cup

1 1/4 cups coarsely chopped watermelon, well packed
1/4 cup water
1/4 teaspoon ground coriander

Blend all the ingredients together with a hand held immersion blender or food processor. Enjoy!

Effects: on a hot summer day, very calming to Pitta; in moderation, neutral for Vata; neutral to diuretic for Kapha. In cold or damp weather, watermelon's cool, heavy qualities will increase Kapha and Vata.

This fruit drink supports: plasma; diuretic, soothes and cleanses achy kidneys. Soothing for cystitis and can be taken 2 – 3 times per day for this purpose (The Lads, 201).

Comments: Best taken on an empty stomach.

CANTALOUPE SPICE VARIATION: Proceed as above, yet substitute 1 1/4 cups ripe cantaloupe for the watermelon.

Effects: calms Vata and Pitta, neutral for Kapha once per week. It could increase Kapha if taken daily.

This drink supports: plasma and hydration.

Comments: While most melons are cooling, cantaloupe is not. It has a sweet taste, a warm virya, and a sweet vipak; it is heavy and watery. In general, it is best for Vata and Pitta. Here, the cool coriander spice makes the recipe digestible for all doshas.

Note: Thanks to Gordon Bruen for the original inspiration on this.

GORD'S STRAWBERRY LEMONADE

Time: 5 minutes
Makes: One quart, serves 4

3 – 4 large ripe, organic strawberries, chopped
1/8 ripe banana
1/3 cup lemon or lime juice
1 1/2 Tablespoons organic coconut sugar or other sweetener
3 cups pure water

Thoroughly whip together all the ingredients in a blender. Serve.

Effects: calms Vata and Pitta, neutral for Kapha.

This drink supports: plasma (hydration), blood cells, energy.

Comments: This light, yet not-too-sweet beverage is best taken by Kapha in small amounts. An easy way to do this is to enjoy a few ounces diluted in mineral water. Mineral water is fine in moderation for Pitta and Kapha, yet it's best avoided by Vata. (Lad, vol. 2, 119)

THE VIRGIN POMEGRITA

This drink is light, refreshing and superbly cooling.

Time: 5 minutes
Makes: 2 cups

    2 Tablespoons organic lime juice
    1/2 cup pure pomegranate juice
    2 teaspoons organic coconut sugar or blue agave syrup
    1/4 - 1/2 teaspoon ground coriander
    1 1/2 cups pure water

Whip together all the ingredients. Serve cool or at room temperature.

Option: simply stir or shake the ingredients together. Although the result is not as frothy, it's just as refreshing.

Effects: In summer, calming to all doshas, especially Pitta. In other seasons, calms Pitta, neutral for Vata & Kapha.

This drink supports: plasma, blood cells, female & male reproductive systems.

COOL-THAT-RAKTA GREEN LIMEADE

This easy, pretty, and delicious drink restores electrolytes in hot weather.

Time: 5 minutes
Makes: 1 cup

> 1/4 cup fresh cilantro
> 1 very thin slice fresh ginger root
> 1 cup organic coconut water
> 2 teaspoons lime juice
> 1/8 teaspoon mineral salt (optional)

Wash and finely chop the cilantro and ginger. Blend them well with the coconut water, lime juice, and mineral salt. Strain. Serve cool or at room temperature.

Effects: calms Pitta big time, calms Vata, neutral for Kapha.

This drink supports: plasma, blood cells. Excellent source of electrolytes in hot weather or when exercising. Mildly diuretic.

Note: Thanks to Shruthi Bajaj, instructional design training analyst and ASCE graduate, for her insights on this one.

SPORTS SOLUTION YEAR-ROUND

Tasty and revivifying.

Time: 5 minutes
Serves: 4

    3 3/4 cups organic coconut water
    1/4 cup lime or lemon juice
    1 Tablespoon maple syrup
    1/16 teaspoon mineral salt
    1 thin slice fresh ginger root (optional)

Combine all the ingredients in a 1-quart glass jar. Shake and serve.

Effects: calms Vata and Pitta, neutral for Kapha in moderation.

This drink supports: plasma and electrolyte balance.

Comments: Mineral-rich coconut water and maple syrup complement the potassium of the citrus juice and the sodium of the salt. This all-natural, isotonic, carbohydrate-balanced solution can be used post-workout for repletion of electrolytes, or pre-work out if you're heading to the gym straight from work.

Here's the breakout of nutrients per cup serving:

Carbohydrate = 12.7 grams, Potassium = 486 mg, Sodium = 111 mg

ADAPTOGEN VARIATION: Add 25 drops of Eleuthero Siberian ginseng tincture per cup to the brew. Shake and serve.

KAPHA VARIATION: Skip the salt and maple syrup to reduce Kapha. Or, to minimize carbohydrates, use less maple syrup.

Notes: With much appreciation to Renee Lynn for inspiration on this drink. (See CHERRY AGUA FRESCA, THE TROPICANA, *and* RASA-RESTORING VEGGIE DRINK *for other coconut water-based beverages.*)

In Mexico, traditional agua frescas infuse the flavor of fresh vegetables or fruits into pure water. They are especially popular in summer.

CUCUMBER AGUA FRESCA

Time: 5 minutes,
plus 2 – 4 hours to infuse
Makes: 2 cups, easy to multiply

1 organic cucumber (2 cups)
2 cups water or organic coconut water
4 teaspoons chopped fresh dill leaf or 2 Tbsp. chopped fresh cilantro

Wash the cucumber well and slice it into a 1-quart glass jar. Add the water and dill (or cilantro). Put in the refrigerator and allow to cold infuse for 2 – 4 hours. Drink the fresh water (agua fresca) and eat the cucumber or use in another dish.

Effects: balances all doshas. In excess, it could increase Kapha.

This drink supports: hydration, cooling, plasma.

Comments: Cucumber is cool and sweet, yet its skin is bitter. To make this drink friendlier for Vata, remove the peel.

CHERRY AGUA FRESCA

Time: 30 minutes to pit,
overnight to infuse
Makes: 1 cup

1 cup fresh organic tart cherries
1 cup organic coconut water

1/8 teaspoon nutmeg
1 teaspoon maple syrup

Wash and pit the cherries. Place them in a glass jar with the coconut water. Infuse in the refrigerator up to 24 hours for maximum flavor. Strain the fluid, reserving the fruit for use in other dishes (ex: VATA CLASSICO SHAKE). Stir the nutmeg and maple syrup into the fresh fruit water. Drink warm before bedtime for a gently restful effect.

Effects: calms Vata, neutral for Kapha and Pitta.

This drink supports: plasma, blood cells, nerves, sleep.

Comments: Organic is essential to infuse nutrients, not pesticides, into the fluid. Melatonin-rich cherries warm up Pitta, yet here coconut water cools the balance.

Note: Thanks to Carry Kim, author of the forthcoming Return to Nature: A Raw & Traditional Foods Cookbook, *yoga teacher, and ASCE for her input on this recipe.*

MANGO AGUA FRESCA VARIATION: Infuse 1 peeled, chopped organic mango in 1 cup coconut water overnight. Strain. Stir in 1/8 teaspoon cardamom. Tridoshic. Entirely delicious.

CUCUMBER DELIGHT

*This frothy white traditional East Indian beverage
tastes wonderful and cools superbly.*

Time: 5 minutes
Makes: 1 1/2 cups

    1 cup organic cow's milk or unsweetened almond milk
    1/2 organic cucumber
    1 teaspoon organic coconut sugar
    1/8 teaspoon ground cardamom

Peel the cucumber and cut it into pieces. Blend it with the rest of the ingredients. Drink immediately.

Effects: with almond milk, tridoshic. Cow's milk, calms Vata and Pitta; increases Kapha.

This beverage supports: cooling, plasma, blood cells, bone.

Comments: Cucumber has a sweet taste, a cooling virya, and a cooling vipak. It relieves thirst and heat; it is diuretic (Tirtha, 137).

Note: While cucumber has many admirable qualities, it rarely crosses my husband's or my palate. When we first tried this recipe, we were astounded. It tastes so good! And we were immediately cooler. The original recipe in Dr. Vasant Lad's Textbook of Ayurveda *(vol. 3, p. 121) calls for rock candy as the sweetener.*

VATA VARIATION: For those who prefer a salty taste to sweet, instead of the coconut sugar, use 1/8 teaspoon mineral salt. Thank you, Shruthi Bajaj.

POMEGRANATE CHIA SMOOTHIE

An unexpectedly tasty, cooling drink.

Time: Minimum of 1-hour soak to maximum of overnight for soaking, plus 5 minutes
Makes: 1 1/2 cups

3/4 cup organic pomegranate juice for the soak
1 Tablespoon chia seeds for the soak
1/4 cup organic grapefruit juice
1/2 cup whole red or purple grapes
    OR 1/2 ripe banana
1/8 teaspoon ground coriander
1/8 teaspoon ground cardamom

Soak the pomegranate juice and the chia seeds together overnight or for a minimum of one hour. Blend with the rest of the ingredients until smooth.

For more protein, soak an additional 1 Tablespoon hemp seeds with the chia seeds.

Effects: neutral for all doshas.

Supports: plasma, blood (especially with the grapes), energizing!, reproductive tissue.

ALOE VARIATION: Skip the banana, and add 1 Tablespoon aloe vera juice to deepen the rejuvenation and cleansing actions. Thanks to Manon Pierme.

PEACH HEMP SHAKE

Time: Overnight soak plus 5 minutes
Serves: 2

2 Tablespoons to 1/4 cup hemp seeds for the soak
1 cup unsweetened almond or commercial flax milk for the soak
1 to 1 1/2 large ripe peaches
1 thin slice fresh ginger
1 teaspoon maple syrup
1/16 teaspoon ground clove (optional)
1/4 teaspoon ground cinnamon (optional)
1/4 teaspoon ground cardamom (optional)

Soak the hemp seeds in the milk overnight or all day in the refrigerator. Once the seeds have soaked, prep the rest of your ingredients. Set aside 1/4 peach in chunks for garnish.

Use an immersion blender or food processor to blend together the seed - milk combination with all ingredients - save the garnish. Float a peach chunk in each cup.

Effects: calms Vata and Pitta. For Kapha, dilute the almond milk 1:1 with water.

This drink supports: elimination (laxative), plasma, muscle, energy, healthy pregnancy, and lactation.

Comments: Peaches are sweet, astringent and definitely calm Vata. 2 - 3 peaches/week are fine for most everyone. Beyond this, Ayurvedic opinions diverge. Dr. Lad says sour and warming (the Lads, 197), as does Swami Tirtha (132). Yet Harish Johari described them as cooling, and used them to calm fever. (31) Ripe nectarines calm Pitta more.

MONSOON VARIATION: When the weather is damp, be sure to add the optional spices listed above, to enhance a possibly dulled digestive fire.

MANGO HEMP VARIATION: In tribute to Harish Johari and *The Healing Cuisine*, here's a riff. Soak the hemp seeds and almond milk as described, then blend them with 1 cup mango, 1 teaspoon finely chopped ginger root, 1 Tablespoon organic rose petals or rose water, 1/4 teaspoon ground cardamom.
Effects: energizing, tridoshic (Johari, 241).

HARI MINT LASSI!

"Yummy and refreshing" is what our taste testers called this.

Time: 5 minutes
Makes: 1 cup, serves 1 - 2

> 15 – 20 (1 Tablespoon) finely chopped fresh mint leaves
> 1/4 - 1 teaspoon peeled and finely chopped fresh ginger (less for Pitta)
> 1/8 teaspoon ground, unroasted cumin
> 1/2 cup plain yogurt (coconut yogurt can also be used)
> 1/2 cup water
> 1 teaspoon organic coconut sugar (optional) or 1/16 teaspoon mineral salt

In a blender, grind the mint, ginger and cumin into a paste with a little yogurt. Add the rest of the ingredients and serve at room temperature or cool.

Effects: calms Vata, neutral for Pitta and Kapha if taken occasionally.

Supports: digestion, plasma, bone.

Notes: This is based on the Hari Lassi recipe in Madhur Jaffrey's Quick & Easy Indian Cooking *(2007). While the lassi starts out with a mild flavor, the after effect in the mouth is pleasantly spicy. Why use unroasted cumin? It has the mildest flavor. If you want a stronger, nuttier taste, roast whole cumin and crush it as instructed in the original recipe. (For more insights about "what form of spice to use when" see another Madhur Jaffrey cookbook,* An Invitation to Indian Cooking, *p.8, (1973)).*

OFF-THE-GRID VARIATION: If you haven't got an electric blender (or electricity), you can grind the mint, ginger and cumin by hand in a mortar and pestle. Then, add a little yogurt, work it into a paste, and stir in the rest of the ingredients. Ayurvedic chef Michele Schulz (www.mapetitecuisinesaine.com) uses an even simpler set up when she's on the road: a glass or small bowl as the mortar with a hand-held wooden citrus juicer as the pestle. In all cases, enjoy!

Time: Overnight soak, plus 5 minutes
Makes: 2 cups

    2 Tablespoons chia seeds for the soak
    2 Tablespoons raw almonds for the soak
    1 cup water for the soak plus 1 teaspoon mineral salt
    1 1/2 cups organic coconut water (use water for Kapha)
    1 ripe mango (1/2 cup)
    1/4 teaspoon ground cardamom

For a breakfast shake, soak the seeds, nuts, water and salt together overnight. Alternatively, for a late afternoon snack, start the soak in the morning.

Once the soak is complete, drain the seeds; discard the soak water. Blend the soaked seeds, nuts and a little coconut water to a paste. A hand-held immersion blender works fine. Add the remaining ingredients and blend well.

Effects: tridoshic, calms all doshas in moderation. Kapha would be wise to use water and a little fresh ginger root instead of coconut water if this is being used daily.

This shake supports: digestive system, energy, mucus membranes, plasma, blood cells, muscle, reproductive system. It is a mild aphrodisiac.

Comments: Ripe mango is sweet and heating with a sweet vipak (long term effect). Its warmth is moderated here by the sweet, cooling coconut water. Coconut water is especially calming to Vata and Pitta, being cool (helping Pitta), sweet and heavy (grounding to both doshas).This drink is gently building, thanks to its overall sweet vipak. If you want a more cooling effect for Pitta, separately soak and peel the almonds. With their peel, they are still energizing, yet warmer in inner action.

RICH VATA VARIATION: Substitute an equal amount of anti-oxidant rich Brazil nuts for the almonds and 1 ripe banana for the mango. Mix in 1/2 teaspoon chopped fresh ginger root and 1/4 teaspoon ground cinnamon.

HIBISCUS SUN COOLER *YEAR-ROUND*

Time: as a sun tea/cold infusion, 2 – 4 hours
Makes: 1 quart

> 2 Tablespoons each: hibiscus flowers (*Hibiscus sabdariffa*), well packed or powdered
> organic rose buds or petals
> fresh mint leaves
> 1 1/4 inch-thick slice fresh ginger (less for Pitta)
> Close to 4 cups water
> Organic sweetener of your choice: coconut sugar, honey, stevia, blue agave syrup

Place all the herbs in a 1-quart glass jar. Add water almost to the top, leaving at least 1/2 inch of breathing space. Put the tea out in the sun to infuse. Steep it until it's as strong as you like. Strain and add a sweetener to taste. Store in the refrigerator.

Effects: balances all doshas.

This drink supports: plasma, blood, muscle, heart, nerves and marrow, hair growth, reproductive system (especially for women). Aphrodisiac, cooling, emmenagogue.

Comments: This outstanding drink from Renee Lynn is rich in antioxidants, reduces inflammation in the tissues, and can help lower high cholesterol and blood pressure. It clears heat and toxins from the blood, while purifying the circulation and heart.

DELICIOUS VARIATION: Mix this drink half and half with grapefruit juice.

GARDENER'S VARIATION: Use fresh rose petals and mint from your organic plants.

QUICK VARIATION FOR BIGGER GROUPS, Renee's original recipe:

Time: 15 minutes. **Makes:** 7 cups. Use: 8 cups water, 1/2 cup hibiscus flowers, 1/4 cup organic rose buds, 1/4 cup mint leaves, 2 Tablespoons grated fresh ginger root (less for Pitta)

In a large pot, bring the water to a boil. Reduce heat to simmer (below boiling) and add the herbs. Simmer for 10 minutes and remove from heat. Let cool, strain and sweeten to taste. Put the tea in a 64-ounce glass pitcher and top off with water, storing in the refrigerator. You can dilute this flavorful tea to taste.

PITTA CALMING TEA MIX

This recipe serves a crowd. For a single serving, see the variation below.

Time: 15 minutes initially, 3 – 5 minutes thereafter
Makes: 12 servings,
one heaping teaspoon mix per serving

2 Tablespoons ground *guduchi*
1 Tablespoon whole cumin seeds
1 Tablespoon whole coriander seeds
1 Tablespoon whole fennel seeds
1/2 teaspoon ground cardamom
1 Tablespoon dried organic rose petals

Make up the mix by measuring out all the spices. Combine and store in a glass jar. This mix will make 12 servings. You can enjoy it for close to 2 weeks. To make a daily serving, bring a cup of water to boil, add 1 heaping teaspoon of the mix, steep 3 minutes or more, strain and enjoy. Dose: one cup per day.

Effects: calms all doshas, especially Pitta.

Supports: digestion, plasma, blood, liver, bone, reproduction, immunity, ojas, longevity.

Comments: an excellent tea for clearing summer heat and skin problems.

Note: With appreciation to Rupen Rao and Aparna Pattewar, ayurveda cookbook (2015). This is a riff on their Pitta herbal tea.

Caution: not for use in pregnancy (as guduchi is contraindicated).

VARIATION FOR ONE: 1/2 teaspoon ground guduchi, 1/4 teaspoon whole cumin seeds. 1/4 teaspoon whole coriander seeds, 1/4 teaspoon whole fennel seeds, a pinch of ground cardamom, and 1/4 teaspoon dried organic rose petals.

Make as above. Relax and enjoy in a cool, soothing place.

MONSOON CHAI YEAR-ROUND

In late summer, drinks that were so appealing earlier in the season can feel too cold, heavy or moist as the rains start. This beverage offers some refreshing relief.

Time: 10 minutes
Serves: 4

1/4 teaspoon ground cinnamon
1/4 teaspoon ground cardamom
2 bay leaves
1/2 inch fresh ginger root
1 Tablespoon raw dandelion root
1 Tablespoon organic jasmine flowers
3 cups water
1 cup organic milk (I use unsweetened almond)
Sweetener to taste (I use 1 Tablespoon organic coconut sugar per pot)

Measure out the spices into one small bowl. Bring the water to a boil in a saucepan. Stir in the spices and simmer for 4 minutes. Pour the tea through a strainer into another clean container, pressing the spices against the strainer with a wooden spoon, to get as much of their essence in the chai as possible. Discard the spices. Put the tea back in the saucepan and add the milk. Heat until hot yet not boiling. Sweeten to taste.

Effects: tridoshic, good for damp heat, could mildly increases Vata in excess.

This sattvic tea supports: digestion, digestive fire, liver, gallbladder, nerves. It calms mood, especially anxiety, and supports spiritual practice.

Comments: When the monsoon begins in mid- to late summer, it's a tricky time for digestion. While the weather is still hot and overall strength is low, agni can be dull and at its ebb. At the same time, Vata is beginning to gather and aggravate, under the heat of Pitta. This milk tea uses the traditional digestive mix of Trisugandhi Churna *(cinnamon, cinnamon leaf or bay leaf, cardamom) to relieve Vata and* manda agni, *while nourishing the liver and nerves. (Jasmine flowers are caffeine-free, unlike the leaves.)*

Notes: This is a dance between Usha Lad's traditional chai and Dr. Frawley's Trisugandhi formula (Ayurvedic Healing, 277) with some twists of jasmine from Amadea.

TULSI LONGEVITY TEA VARIATION: Substitute 1 Tablespoon tulsi and 1 teaspoon amalaki for the jasmine Prepare as above.

Effects: tridoshic. This tea supports: digestion, liver, heart, all dhatus, and ojas.

HYDRATION PLUS VEGGIE JUICE

Time: 15 minutes
Makes: 2 cups

You need a juicer for this recipe.

1/2 large jicama (3 cups)
1 cup well-packed lettuce, raw spinach or other raw greens
1/2 organic cucumber
2 stalks of celery
1 thin slice fresh ginger root
2 Tablespoons fresh basil leaves (optional)
1 Tablespoon lime or lemon juice

Wash the vegetables and peel the jicama. Juice all the vegetables, ginger and basil. Stir in the lime or lemon juice.

Effects: relieves excess Pitta and Kapha; neutral for Vata in extreme moderation.

Supports: plasma, blood cells and hydration.

Comments: Fresh herbs can serve as effective and flavorful digestive aids in fresh juice. I've found that mildly pungent herbs like the fresh basil or Tulsi basil in this recipe are best used in later summer, to warm rising Vata. Earlier in the year, in late spring and early summer, herbs that are cooling seem best absorbed, like the mint in RAKTA-REVIVING VEGGIE JUICE, p. 64. Jicama has sweet and astringent tastes, a cooling virya, and a sweet vipak. It is great for summer and Pitta. It also contains copper and iron, used to build red blood cells.

BLUEBERRY APPLE BLISS

A bright, sweet, simple dessert

Time: 10 minutes, plus 1 hour for it to set up
Makes: 2 cups, serves 4 polite people

> 1 large sweet apple
> 1 cup fresh blueberries
> 3/4 cup organic coconut water
> 1 teaspoon fresh lemon juice
> 1/16 teaspoon ground cinnamon (optional)
> 1/2 Tablespoon organic lemon zest (optional)

Wash the fruit well. Chop the apple. Set aside a few pieces of fruit as a garnish. Blend all ingredients until smooth and pour into four small serving cups. Cool 1 hour or more in the refrigerator where the purée will set up like a pudding. If you like, you can take the cups out of the refrigerator to allow them to return to room temperature before serving.
Garnish with fruit pieces.

Effects: tridoshic, balances all doshas.

This dish supports: energy, plasma, ligaments.

Comments: Both blueberry and apple are naturally high in pectin. This causes them to gel readily on their own. The pectin also provides a gentle fiber action that cleanses the colon. This dessert will cure whatever ails you. It is rich in vitamin C, potassium and manganese. Enjoy in warm - not cold - weather.

Notes: Thanks to Michele Schulz for so many things, including the name of this dish!

FAUX BOBA

Here's a healing, Ayurvedic take on the popular Taiwanese "bubble tea".

Time: start 2 hours(!) before
you want to enjoy this

Serves: 4

1/3 cup organic tapioca pearls (the largest you can find)
1 1/2 cups water
1/16 teaspoon mineral salt
1/8 teaspoon each ground cinnamon and ground cardamom
2 Tablespoons organic coconut sugar
1/2 cup water
3 teabags of your favorite organic herbal or decaf tea (I like Organic India's Tulsi Peppermint or a Chai Rooibos, or the MONSOON CHAI in this book)
2 cups organic unsweetened almond milk or milk of your choice

In a bowl, wash the tapioca well. Rinse it twice, drain it well, then set it aside to rest for one hour. If it rests longer, this is also fine.

Bring the 1 1/2 cups of water and salt to a boil in a medium saucepan. Stir in the tapioca pearls and spices as if you were making pasta. Keep stirring over medium low heat until the tapioca pearls are soft and clear, about 10 minutes. Turn off the heat.

Stir the coconut sugar into the tapioca. Let the flavors percolate for a half hour or more, stirring occasionally so that the tapioca doesn't set up into a mass.

While the sugar and tapioca are melding, make your tea concentrate: boil 1/2 cup of water and steep the 3 tea bags of your choice in it for 5 minutes. Discard the teabags. Stir the 2 cups of milk into the tea concentrate, then stir the milk tea into the tapioca, gently dislodging the sticky pearls so they float freely in the liquid. Serve warm.

Effects: tridoshic. This drink supports: digestion, plus all tissues after illness.

Comments: In Ayurveda, tapioca is valued as a nourishing food for fasting days, breakfast, and convalescence. Sweet and astringent in taste, it has a cooling virya and a sweet vipak. It is especially calming for Pitta and Kapha. Here, the milk and spices balance it for Vata. For optimal digestion, do not combine tapioca with grains or fruit.

Notes: See Usha Lad and Dr. Vasant Lad's Ayurvedic Cooking for Self Healing *for the best ways to prepare tapioca.*

Autumn: Integration

Gathering together

As we head into autumn, I wanted to know how the fellow travelers in this book were faring. Aimee, the young farmer who opened our winter chapter, has been growing tulsi basil and ashwagandha in her greenhouse this year. She is ready to start offering her own tea blends, herbal salves and creams at the local farmer's market this coming winter. When asked about any insights she wanted to share with readers, she focused on how to work with Vata in fall. "As it gets colder, my stomach often gets triggered. I've definitely noticed that drinking warm, spicy teas is helpful, like the herbal chais or ginger tea. Warm really makes a difference." She's planning on farming less in the coming year and making herbal products more.

Therapist and teacher Ralph emailed back, "Like in spring, my "Sense of Self" is excited about the change. In the fall, so many people do their final transition, become ill, over-stress, and . . . are joyful. It's time to go inward . . . and to *deeply connect* (with) yoga, cross country skiing, pranayama exercises (like bhastrika, agnisar, kapalabhati), chanting, meditation, writing, listening to my favorite tunes, and baking. (As an) Agent Orange / PTSD Veteran, it's upmost important that I don't stop riding the Healing Tiger."

Tim, the herbalist, spoke about "the importance of doing 'PM in the AM'. That's 'prayer and meditation', in the morning," he explained. While in warmer seasons he likes to do this outside, now it's not as easy to step out into the cool of the morning. He was heartened to discover a suitable spot inside. Looking at the myriad of difficulties that people encounter, he advised, "Remember these barriers are real, yet they may be temporary." When asked about this season, he replied with a smile, "I'm not going to run away just because it's autumn! We'll meet these (changes) head-on."

Elder Margie is looking forward to fall, her favorite season. "Well, fall and spring, they're both great." While still not a drinker of herbal teas, Ayurvedic or otherwise, she loved the HEART-FELT SMOOTHIE from the autumn recipes. "It's delicious."

In terms of staying balanced, she said, "For me, it's about continuing to "exercise" (keep moving), to eat nutritious foods and drinks, and to keep taking the nutrients that Amadea recommends, which I believe have contributed to my good health. Finally, it's about living in a place I love where I can be close to nature and see it unfold daily. This, too, nourishes my spirit greatly."

We've danced together through this whole year of nourishing beverages. Now we come to autumn, the final season in this *Easy Healing Drinks* book. How are you doing?

Meet the rhythm of the season

As you can see in The Rhythm of Agni Through the Seasons, pages 69 – 73, Vata is now manifesting fully and agni is beginning to return in strength. While Pitta dips drastically, Kapha is inching its way upward, to peak again in winter. Right now it is mostly hidden under the guise of Vata's predominance. What does this mean for us practically?

With autumn and climate change, we need to keep flexible and open to whatever conditions Nature presents us. While Vata is the key dosha for enhancing flexibility, it is also the dosha that can get most disrupted by changes, small or large. With unusual shifts in heat and cold, hurricanes, thunderstorms or fires can surprise us. With climate change, weather patterns can persist longer in an area and be more extreme than in past decades. We may have to let go of our preconceptions about the season and our place in it. All this particularly impacts Vata, which thrives on safety and security for grounding. The safety we create now may be more of an inner state, as we begin to nurture "openness free of fixation" as one Tibetan Buddhist practice invites. In their replies, both Tim and Ralph wisely touch on this need for inner balance.

Outwardly in autumn, from a practical fashion standpoint, we've got to be ready with the layered look. Vata can easily get chilly, yet Pitta may tear off the jacket. Kapha will still be yearning for fresh air and pleasant breezes. If we can, this outward focus may go beyond the weather to include an open acceptance of whatever is arising and generosity to who needs what now.

As Vata holds strong, coming out from under Pitta's bright light of summer, we're a bit back to where we began last winter: more warm drinks, more focus on grounding. Yet there are some subtle differences, too. It's Vata's season now, not Kapha's, as it was in winter. Vata dosha thrives on sweet, sour and salty tastes. As we described in the summer section, sour and salty tastes nurture agni that has been steadily rising (we hope) since summer. This fresh agni will peak this coming winter.

In this chapter, beverages like FIVE-SPICE MISO BROTH (a little salty), CLEASING ALMOND GREEN DRINK, HEART-FELT TEA, and HEART-FELT SMOOTHIE (all a bit sour) and MAGIC YAM KHIR (sweet and nourishing to ojas) are here to support you in this season. This fall recipe collection opens with PAPAYA PLEASURE, PAPAYA DETOX and makes use of this fruit's great ability to calm an uncertain gut. BLACK SESAME SEED SHAKE puts the focus back on building after a couple of seasons of eating more lightly.

A new kind of smoothie

Plant-based foods are rich in minerals, fiber, vitamins, and color. Related to this, I'd like to include one more chunk of information here before we head into the fall recipes. Over the course of growing this book, I've evolved a new Ayurvedic approach for making the kind of smoothies Westerners love, yet using more digestible whole plant foods. There are key differences in the production and ingredients of these smoothies. You can make and enjoy these drinks easily, too. They include:

1. **Easier simpler food combinations**

2. **Whole foods rather than processed ones**

3. **Omega 3-rich ingredients**

4. **Generous amounts of natural fiber**

5. **Digestion-enhancing, rejuvenating spices**

First point: Everyone's gut is different. Some of us can get used to digesting combinations that would never work in another's system. That said, a strong focus of Ayurveda is optimizing digestion for anyone. Examples of food combinations that are considered tough to digest and absorb include: milk with yogurt, milk or yogurt with banana, milk or yogurt with fruit in general. Does this sound like your average morning smoothie or what? Adding digestive spices like cinnamon or ginger can help with these combinations, yet why stress your gut first thing? If you could use something that is easier to digest and absorb, would you be willing to do it?

Nuts, seeds and fruit do well together, so if you tolerate these, they're great to use in smoothies. Banana with almond milk (THE VATA CLASSICO), citrus with coconut (COOLING COCONUT GREEN DRINK) and apples with nuts (APPLE SPICE SMOOTHIE) are all friendly combinations.

If you want to use fermented dairy (ie. yogurt or kefir) in your smoothie, try it with veggies and/or spices, rather than fruit. Here are a few delicious and innovative examples: ROSY BEET SMOOTHIE, ZESTY LEMONGRASS CARROT SMOOTHIE, SPEEDY PACHAK LASSI, and the CAULIFLOWER SMOOTHIE.

Second point: Not everybody's stomach nor bank account can digest high-end protein powders. Yet protein can be important, if you're a growing person (i.e. toddler, child, teenager, pregnant or nursing mom) or are looking to stabilize your energy. I'm not talking about vast swaths of protein, yet enough to feel sustained. (This may feel like a more important point for the blood type O's among us.) When wanting to add extra protein, I've come to appreciate the value of seeds and nuts, especially hemp seeds. At 5 grams of protein per tablespoon, it competes well with a small egg. See PEACH HEMP SHAKE or GREEN BASIL BREW for ideas here.

Third point: If sustainably harvested fish oil gives you the burps, what's an alternative to getting your mood-enhancing Omega 3's? (If you can tolerate fish oils, I do recommend them.) Or, fish oils may just not be your choice should you be a plant-based eater. It's

very easy to up your Omega's in smoothies by using chia seeds (especially for Kapha and Pitta) or flax seeds (for Vata). Chia seeds in particular can give the delightful thickness that usually is associated with dairy products without the heaviness dairy often provides. Check out the Kapha version of the COCAMOLE SMOOTHIE.

Fourth point: Putting more *real* fresh fruits, veggies, nuts, or seeds in your drinks gives you more energy-rich prana, as well as fiber. Just about every recipe in this book is an example of this. If you want to get really wild and crazy, there's even a fiber-rich mung bean drink (see GREEN TARA SHAKE, COOK'S VARIATION).

Fifth point: Spices help ignite agni, our digestive fire. They can also rejuvenate specific depleted tissues, whether that be your adrenals, reproductive system or liver. We go past just adding a sprinkling of spices to a drink. We've thought about how each drink can support specific needs. One of the easiest ways to make a truly rejuvenative brew is to start with tasty, deeply healing Ayurvedic teas. Use them as the liquid base in your smoothie, rather than water, juice, or milk. Notice how you feel using this alternative. This technique is best used with the teas designated here as "rejuvenative", rather than "cleansing." For example, you don't want to get in the way of cleansing teas by throwing extra banana or almond butter under their tires as they squeal into action. The rejuvenative teas, on the other hand, are there to build, so strengthening ingredients like banana and almond butter can be an enhancement. Here are some healing cases in point: the HEART-FELT SMOOTHIE, RASAYANA SMOOTHIE (see MAN'S YAB TEA) or EASY REJUVENATIVE SMOOTHIE (found with the WOMAN'S YUM TEA).

Seed soaking for both building and cleansing

There's got to be a down side to all this goodness, right? Well, actually there is. Although nuts, seeds, grains, and legumes have many fine qualities, they also tend to be abundant sources of phytic acid. Phytic acid is naturally present in plants to protect them from premature sprouting. Indeed a plant's mission is to sprout, grow, fruit, produce seed. However, if they sprout too soon, none of the maturing may happen. In a human gut, phytic acid is problematic as it can inhibit mineral absorption. What to do? Soak seeds to make them more absorbable and reduce their phytic acid content as much as 50%. For more about soaking seeds for digestibility and healing, see: https://wellnessmama.com/59139/soaking-nuts-seeds/

How to soak nuts or seeds for a single serving of a smoothie:

2 Tablespoons nuts or seeds

1/2 teaspoon mineral salt

1 cup warm water

Put all ingredients together in a clean glass jar with a lid, shake and let them sit overnight or all day (8-12 hours). The soaked nuts/seeds will be waiting for you when you need them, either first thing in the morning or after work or school. Drain, discarding the soaking water in which the phytic acid has dissolved. Then blend the nuts/seeds into whatever smoothie you've chosen to make. Simple. This works well for any hulled nut, sesame, sunflower, pumpkin, or hemp seed. Once you get in the habit of soaking your seeds, it's easy. You can choose a different seed each day if you like.

Don't try this method with chia or flax seeds. They simply glop up and hold on to all the liquid and salt. Bless them and use them for what they are good for: Omega 3-richness, thickening, fiber and protein.

If the weather is very hot, put the soak solution in the refrigerator. Otherwise, warm water is best for clearing away the phytic acid to improve mineral absorption. It also starts the healthy sprouting process making nuts/seeds even more digestible.

Quick soak method: Bring water to a boil and pour it over the seeds/nuts and salt in a small bowl or glass jar. Soak while preparing the rest of whatever recipe you're making. The slower method is preferable for prana and digestibility, yet in a pinch, this works.

For simple, healthy, Ayurvedic smoothies, start by soaking the seeds, then make your favorite rejuvenative tea. When you're ready for the smoothie, just add some fruit or veggies, and you've got it. Bon appétit!

Thank you for joining us,

Amadea and Renee

Autumn Recipes

PAPAYA PLEASURE, PAPAYA DETOX

Time: 5 minutes
Makes: 1 cup plus

    1 cup fresh ripe papaya chunks, preferably organic
    1/2 cup water
    1/2 teaspoon coconut sugar
    1/8 teaspoon ground cardamom

Blend the papaya chunks to a pulp with an immersion or hand-held blender. Add the rest of the ingredients. Serve at room temperature or gently warmed.

Effects: calms Vata and Kapha, fine for Pitta once per week.

This drink supports: digestion, energy, elimination.

Comments: This pleasing, traditional drink from the Lads (p. 197) is designed to calm hyperacidity, acute gastritis and indigestion. Not for use in pregnancy, as it contains natural estrogen.

SERIOUS VARIATION: Instead of the coconut sugar, add 2 teaspoons lemon juice and 1 Tablespoon aloe vera juice.

Effects: tridoshic.

This drink supports: deep cleansing, especially helpful for Vata.

Comments: This alkalizing fruit drink cleanses the bones. For Ayurvedic practitioners, this drink could be recommended for conditions when the herb nirgundhi would be used, such as for backache, osteoarthritis, and detox. Cardamom directs the flow of Vata downward (Pole, 151). While this drink tastes serious, if you need it, it tastes good.

SOME LIKE IT HOT, SOME LIKE IT COLD BLUEBERRY SHAKE

Time: Seed soaking, plus 5 minutes
Makes: 2 cups

    2 Tablespoons hemp seeds (options: sunflower or chia seeds)
    1 cup water at room temperature
    1/2 teaspoon mineral salt
    1 cup fresh organic blueberries
    1 cup organic apricot juice (warming) or pomegranate juice (cooling)
    1 teaspoon organic lemon zest (warming) or lime zest (cooling)
    1/8 teaspoon ground cinnamon or nutmeg

Seed Soaking instructions: Pour the water over the hemp seeds and salt in a small bowl or jar. Let sit for 4 hours or more.

Wash the berries. Drain the seeds, discarding the soaking water. Put all ingredients in a blender. Process until smooth.

Effects: The warming version balances Vata and Kapha; it's neutral in effect for Pitta. The cooling version calms Pitta and is neutral for Vata and Kapha.

This alkalizing shake supports: plasma, heart, muscle, ligaments, energy.

Comments: If you use this shake on a regular basis, the soak significantly reduces the phytic acid content of the seeds. Phytic acid protects plants yet can impede the uptake of minerals in humans. If you're using chia seeds, this slow-soak step is not practical, as the chia seeds simply gel up in whatever fluid they're in.

APPLE SPICE SMOOTHIE

Start your day with flavor and fun.

Time: Overnight soak, plus 15 - 20 minutes
Makes: 2 cups

2 Tablespoons almonds, soaked overnight in 1 cup
    warm water and 1/2 teaspoon mineral salt
2 apples
1 thin slice of ginger (skip for Pitta)
1/2 cup water or apricot juice
1 Tablespoon lemon or lime juice
1/4 teaspoon ground cinnamon
1/8 teaspoon ground nutmeg
1 teaspoon organic lemon zest
1 date (optional)
1/2 - 3/4 cup unsweetened organic almond milk
    or water
Ground nutmeg as garnish (optional)

Soak almonds in the water and mineral salt overnight.
Drain, discard the water and peel the almonds.

Wash and thinly slice the apples (no need to peel). Simmer the apples, ginger, water or juice, and spices in
a medium stainless steel saucepan until the apples are tender, about 10 minutes. Add the soaked almonds,
date and almond milk to the saucepan of apples. Stir to mix and remove from heat. With a hand held blender
or any kind of food processor you have, blend until smooth. Serve at room temperature or warm, whichever
is more appealing for you.

Effects: calms Pitta and Kapha, neutral for Vata.

Supports: plasma and hydration, laxative.

GREEN TARA SHAKE

This grounding, rich drink is great for the heart and skin.

Time: 5 minutes
Makes: 1 1/2 cups

1 small avocado
1/4 cup fresh basil
2 Tablespoons fresh parsley
2 Tablespoons lemon or lime juice
1 Tablespoon raw tahini or almond butter
1/4 teaspoon pippali or freshly ground black pepper
1/16 teaspoon mineral salt
3/4 - 1 cup water or more, to desired texture

Combine all the ingredients in a blender, starting with only 3/4 cup water. Add more water as needed to create the silky texture you want, warm or at room temperature.

Effects: calms Vata and Pitta, neutral for Kapha with half the avocado, double the parsley.

This shake supports: digestive system, skin, muscle, heart, fat, and nerves.

Comments: Avocado builds weight while reducing the risk of heart attacks. Astringent and cool, with a pungent vipak, it is best digested with spices like these (Tirtha, 135).

COOK'S VARIATION: Use 1 cup of your favorite cooked mung dal, 1/2 cup chopped cilantro, 2 Tablespoons lemon juice, 1/16 teaspoon chipotle or cayenne chili, and 3/4 cup water (I use warm). Blend as above. Makes 2 cups.

Effects: tridoshic. Tastes really good!

CILANTRO-SUNFLOWER SEED VARIATION: Soak 2 Tablespoons raw sunflower seeds in 1/2 cup warm water for 1 or more hours. Blend with 1/2 cup chopped cilantro, 2 Tablespoons lemon juice, 1 teaspoon light yellow miso (or chickpea miso), 1/16 teaspoon cayenne or chipotle chili, and 3/4 cup water, or enough for desired texture.

Effects: calms Pitta and Vata, neutral for Kapha.

PUMPKIN SPICE SMOOTHIE

Time: Overnight soak, plus 15 - 20 minutes
Makes: 2 cups plus

    2 Tablespoons raw, organic pumpkin seeds, soaked overnight in 1 cup warm water
        and 1/2 teaspoon mineral salt
    1 13- or 15-oz. can organic cooked pumpkin (or 1 3/4 cups freshly made)
    1 cup organic unsweetened almond milk (commercial or homemade) or plain yogurt
    1 1/2 teaspoons organic pumpkin pie spice blend*
    1 Tablespoon organic coconut sugar or raw honey

Soak the pumpkin seeds as above. In the morning, drain, reserve the seeds and discard the water. This soaking process improves mineral absorption.

Heat the pumpkin, milk and spice blend in a medium saucepan until warm. With a hand held blender or any kind of food processor you have, blend the pumpkin mixture with the soaked seeds and sweetener until smooth. Serve at room temperature or warm.

Effects: calms Vata and Pitta, neutral for Kapha.

Supports: mucous membranes, muscle, reproductive system, immunity, laxative.

Comments: This smoothie is rich in beta-carotene and the trace mineral zinc.

Notes: Ayurvedic healing strongly emphasizes fresh food (i.e. freshly cooked pumpkin vs. canned) because there it contains more prana, and therefore, more energy. Yet in my private practice in the US, many of my clients have limited time, finances, and cooking ability, so I created this nourishing drink for them.

* SLOW - MO VARIATION: I was delighted when I found organic pumpkin pie spice in a local grocery for my non-cook people. If this isn't available in your area, try this recipe: 1 teaspoon ground cinnamon, 1/4 teaspoon ground ginger, 1/8 teaspoon ground nutmeg, 1/16 teaspoon ground allspice, and 1/16 teaspoon ground clove. If you only have one of the last two spices, relax and use what you've got. Have fun!

DELICATA CILANTRO SMOOTHIE

This bright, nourishing dish makes a good after-school snack or light dinner.

Time: 30 minutes or more, depending on how you make the squash.
Makes: 2- 3 cups

> 1 cup delicata squash, roasted or steamed
> 1/2 - 1 avocado
> 1/2 cup cilantro, chopped
> 1 Tablespoon fresh ginger, chopped or grated
> 1/4 teaspoon ground turmeric or even better, 1/2 Tablespoon fresh turmeric root, grated
> 1/4 teaspoon pippali or black pepper, freshly ground, to taste
> 1 teaspoon lemon juice (optional)
> 1/4 teaspoon mineral salt (optional)
> 1 – 3 cups water or veggie steaming water, as per preferred texture

Add all the ingredients to a blender, blend and enjoy!

Effects: tridoshic.

This soup-like smoothie supports: blood sugar, heart, lungs, muscle, fat, mucus membranes, immunity and ojas.

Comments: Swami Tirtha considers acorn squash, a delicata relative, tridoshic with its sweet and astringent tastes, cool virya and pungent vipak (Tirtha, 138).

Notes: With much appreciation to Alexandra Stoller, graduate student in acupuncture and cranial-sacral work, for this satisfying recipe. Our testers loved it, especially those on the mend.

THE COCAMOLE FAMILY OF SMOOTHIES

Rich and delicious wholesome drinks for after school,
after work or before bedtime.

Dosha	VATA	PITTA	KAPHA
	1 Tablespoon raw sesame, sunflower or pumpkin seeds	2 Tablespoons raw sunflower or pumpkin seeds	
	1 Tablespoon or more flax seeds	1 Tablespoon chia seeds (optional)	2 - 3 Tablespoons chia seeds
	2 cups almond milk or 1 cup almond milk and 1 cup whole milk	1 cup water or yam water plus 1 cup organic coconut water	2 cups favorite spicy tea, *we use Tulsi Red Chai Masala (non-caffeinated)*
	1 cup yam, roasted or simmered	2/3 cup yam, roasted or simmered	1/2 cup yam, roasted or simmered
	1/4 teaspoon ground cinnamon + 1 thin slice of fresh ginger	1/2 teaspoon ground cardamom	1/4 teaspoon ground cinnamon + 1 thin slice of fresh ginger
	2 Tablespoons carob powder	2 Tablespoons carob powder	2 Tablespoons carob powder
	1 teaspoon raw honey or coconut sugar or 1 packet stevia (1 gram)	1 teaspoon coconut sugar (optional)	1/2 teaspoon raw honey or 1 packet stevia (1 gram)
	1/2 teaspoon almond extract	1 teaspoon almond extract	1/2 teaspoon almond extract
Makes	3 thick cups	2 1/2 cups	2 1/2 cups
Effects	Calms V & P, increases K	Calms V & P, increases K	Calms K, neutral P, can increase V

Directions:

Roast or simmer some yams for dinner. Save one small yam to enjoy in this drink the next day. Or, if you're pressed for time, use organic, canned sweet potato. Save the yam's cooking water as you can use it to soak the seeds.

Soak the seeds overnight in water, yam water, almond milk or tea. A glass jar with a lid works well for this. For the Kapha version, make up two cups of tea with two tea bags, steep 10 minutes, remove the tea bags, then stir in the chia seeds.

Once soaked, using a blender or food processor, blend the seeds and liquid until smooth. Then, add the rest of the ingredients and blend again.

All these smoothies support: grounding, energy, ease of digestion and elimination.

Comments: Blending enlivens our digestive fire.

Notes: The inspiration for this drink is molé *(pronounced mo-lay), the sumptuous Mexican sauce named after the indigenous Nahuatl word* molli, *which means "concoction" (Kennedy, 200). Molé usually is made of seeds, chilies, spices and chocolate. Here carob is used instead of the chocolate.*

Try this beverage warm before bedtime with 1/2 teaspoon shankhapushpi/cup.

VARIATIONS: Vata can add 1 – 2 extra Tablespoons flax seed for additional laxative action, bone strength, and Omega 3's for the nerves. Pitta or Vata can add 1 or more Tablespoons hemp seeds for extra protein. Kapha can add as much spice as desired.

BLACK SESAME SHAKE

Time: Overnight soak, plus 5 minutes
Makes: 2 cups, serves 2 - 3

> 1/3 cup black sesame seeds
> 3 Tablespoons hemp seeds
> 2 cups water for the soak
> 1 teaspoon mineral salt for the soak
>
> 1 1/4 - 1 1/2 cup water
> 1 teaspoon – 1 Tablespoon raw honey, to taste
> 1/4 teaspoon ground cardamom

Soak the seeds, water and salt in a glass container all day or overnight. In the morning, or whenever you want to enjoy this, drain off the salt water, reserving only the seeds. Blend the seeds with a little water to make as creamy a paste as possible, then blend in the remaining water, honey, and cardamom until smooth. Enjoy!

Effects: unabashedly Vata-calming. This mildly increases Pitta and Kapha. Use maple syrup or organic coconut sugar for Pitta. Make it thinner with more water for Kapha.

This shake supports: blood cells, skin, muscles, fat, bone, nerves, kidneys, reproductive tract, ojas.

Comments: Sesame seeds have sweet, bitter, and astringent tastes, yet are heating and pungent in their long-term action, making them most calming for Vata. Their oily, heavy, smooth qualities ground this dosha well. This drink strongly builds and calms.

Notes: This recipe has some crunch to it! It is dedicated to the memory of Martha Iwaski, a remarkably skilled healer and acupuncturist. For many years she advised our family to eat purple and black foods with the fall doyo (Japanese for change of seasons). While it can be enjoyed year-round, it is particularly suited for autumn, especially for Vata. An equal amount of raw organic white sesame seeds can be used in place of the black sesame, if you like, for similar yet a bit milder effects.

CLEANSING ALMOND GREEN DRINK

Time: 10 - 15 minutes
Makes: 1 cup

    1/3 cup well-packed cilantro, finely chopped
    1/2 - 1 teaspoon or more peeled and finely chopped fresh ginger
    1 Tablespoon fresh lemon juice
    1 cup organic unsweetened almond milk or the veggie steaming
        water
    1/2 cup or more dark leafy greens of your choice

Steam the greens if you need to keep Vata calm. This step also makes them more digestible for all the doshas. Set them aside. Save the veggie steaming water.

Pre-pulse the cilantro, ginger and lemon juice until they are as smooth as possible. You may need to add a little of the almond milk or veggie steaming water to process this. Add the rest of the almond milk or veggie steaming water; blend until smooth. Now it's time to play: blend in as much of the steamed greens as you like. Enjoy!

Effects: calms Pitta and Kapha, neutral Vata. Raw greens increase Vata, yet steaming them and adding ginger, lemon and almond milk all make this recipe more balancing for Vata.

Supports: plasma, blood cells, muscles, immunity, ojas.

Notes: This is an adaptation of spring's COOLING COCONUT GREEN DRINK, page 47, made warmer for autumn.

To make your own almond milk, see page 25. If you are seeking a high quality, commercial variety, I suggest New Barn brand, found in the refrigerator section of organic stores.

GREEN BASIL BREW

Amadea often makes this calming and satisfying brew

as part of a quick lunch.

Time: 15 – 20 minutes
Makes: 2 cups

  2 Tablespoons sunflower, pumpkin or hemp seeds
  1 cup water for the soak
  1/2 teaspoon mineral salt for the soak
  2 1/2 cups water
  2 cups broccoli
  1/4 inch slice red onion
  1 teaspoon yellow or white miso (soy-free miso is also fine)
  1 Tablespoon dried basil leaves
  1/2 Tablespoon dried oregano leaves

For better absorbability, bring 1 cup of water to a boil and pour it over the seeds and salt in a small bowl or glass jar. Soak while preparing the rest of the drink.

Bring 2 1/2 cups water to a boil in a medium saucepan. Add the broccoli and red onion, cover and simmer until the broccoli is tender and a beautiful green.

Drain the seeds, discarding the soak water. Put them in a blender with a little of the broccoli cooking water and grind into a smooth paste. Add the rest of the ingredients, including the simmered veggies and 2 cups of the cooking water. Blend until smooth. Add extra water as needed for desired consistency. Serve hot.

Effects: calms Pitta and Kapha, neutral for Vata when used once per week.

This drink supports: cleansing in plasma, blood cells, muscle, and fat; builds immunity.

Notes: This GREEN BASIL BREW *has a classic "pizza" flavor. While most pizzas are a little tough on the liver, this dish helps it. If you have a Vitamix or a good grinder, you can create a variation that is even better for the liver by grinding 1 Tablespoon raw organic milk thistle seeds and then blending them in with the rest of the ingredients.*

OJAS MILK *YEAR-ROUND*

This delicious nut drink offers high quality, sattvic rejuvenation

and builds immunity.

Time: Overnight or all-day soak,
plus 15 minutes

Makes: close to 1 quart

1 cup almonds
3 cups water for the soak
1 1/2 teaspoons mineral salt for the soak
4 cups (1 quart) additional water
1 – 2 pitted dates (optional)
1 Tablespoon rose water or organic rose petals
1/2 teaspoon ground cardamom
a few threads of saffron (optional)
1/16 teaspoon mineral salt

You'll need two 1-quart glass jars. In the first, soak the almonds with 3 cups of water and salt overnight (or all day). In the second jar, put the rest of the ingredients to soak together. Stir or shake and let sit.

When you are ready to make the OJAS MILK, drain the nuts, discarding the soak water. Place the soaked almonds plus the ingredients from the second jar in a blender. Blend as smooth as possible. Using a nut milk bag (best for smoothness) or other fine mesh strainer, press the mixture through into a large pot or bowl. You can blend the pulp with some of the freshly strained almond milk again to get more milk out of the pulp. Store in a glass or stainless steel jar in the refrigerator for up to 36 hours.

Effects: calms Vata and Pitta well, moderately increases Kapha.

This milk supports: every tissue, immunity and ojas.

Comments: The majority of the almond peel is eliminated with straining. If you wish to make this even more calming to Pitta, after soaking and before blending, rub off peels.

Notes: This recipe comes from ASCE grad Sulis Cutler, a Polarity and massage therapist, and yoga teacher. http://www.laughingtreespace.com/blog/ *Sulis says, "The pulp is lovely mixed with hot cereal for added heft. Plus drying/dehydrating it is SOOOOO yummy." Michele Schulz of* www.mapetitecuisinesaine.com *integrates the okara, the nut pulp, into cookies, cakes, breads, and sprinkles it over veggies (delicious mashed into a sweet potato), or into smoothies for extra fiber.*

HEART-FELT TEA *YEAR-ROUND*

This robust, lovely red brown tea strengthens the heart on many levels.

Time: 15 - 20 minutes
Serves: 4

1 Tablespoon organic hawthorn berries
1 Tablespoon green rooibos leaves
1 teaspoon tulsi (whole leaves or powder)
1 teaspoon hibiscus flowers
1 teaspoon linden flowers and leaves (optional)

2 slices organic orange, with peel
1/4 teaspoon ground cinnamon
1/4 teaspoon amalaki
1/8 teaspoon ground pippali
4 1/2 cups water
Sweetener to taste

Measure out the spices and fruit into a bowl. Bring the water to a boil in a saucepan. Stir in all the ingredients; simmer for 5 minutes or more. Remove from heat and let it sit 10 minutes or more. Pour the tea through a strainer into a clean container, using a wooden spoon to press the spices against the strainer to squeeze out as much of their essence as possible. Sweeten to taste. Serve hot or cool, with almond milk if you like. It can be stored in a glass jar in a cool place for future use.

Effects: tridoshic.

This sattvic tea supports: heart, plasma, blood, mind, immunity, ojas.

*Comments: This gently sour blend of Eastern and Western plants is heart-centric. Green rooibos (Aspalathus linearis) from Africa has the highest amount of anti-oxidants of any rooibos.(*http://www.vegkitchen.com/nutrition/9-proven-health-benefits-of-rooibos-tea/*) This longevity herb reduces the risk of heart disease, hypertension, and cancer. Tulsi (sacred basil from India) is a cardiac and immune tonic that lifts the spirits. Linden (Tilia cordata) is used therapeutically as an anti-hypertensive and diuretic. Hibiscus purifies the heart both spiritually and physically (Lad & Frawley, 125). Orange cleanses the blood in heart disorders (Tirtha 132). Hawthorn works with amalaki as an excellent heart tonic. Together these two act in the blood to reduce cholesterol and palpitations, while calming the mind (Pole 126). Pippali is a digestive and rejuvenative for plasma, blood and fat (Pole 238). Cinnamon also strengthens the heart.*

HEART-FELT DRY TEA MIX: If you like this tea, here's an easy way to make it up in larger batches as a pre-made mix. In a medium bowl, measure out the dry ingredients: 1/3 cup organic hawthorn berries, 1/3 cup green rooibos leaves, 2 Tablespoons tulsi (whole leaves or powder), 2 Tablespoons hibiscus flowers, 2 Tablespoons linden flowers and leaves (optional), 1 1/2 teaspoon ground cinnamon, 1 1/2 teaspoon amalaki, and 3/4 teaspoon ground pippali. Stir well and store in a dry glass jar.

To serve 4, follow the recipe above. Use 3 Tablespoons of the mix per 4 1/2 cups of water. Add the fresh orange slices as indicated.

HEART-FELT SMOOTHIE   *YEAR-ROUND*

Here's a simple way to drink your herbs and enjoy them, too!

HEART-FELT SMOOTHIE FOR VATA: Once you've made up the HEART-FELT TEA recipe, blend 1 cup of it with 2 Tablespoons soaked raw hemp seeds or sunflower seeds (see How to soak nuts or seeds for a single serving of a smoothie, p. 104). Add 1 ripe banana and blend all ingredients until smooth.

Makes: 1 1/2 cups.

Effects: calms Vata strongly. Mildly increases Pitta and Kapha if taken regularly.

This smoothie supports: heart, skin, plasma, muscle, mind.

Comments: Hemp seeds are a cardiac tonic and nourish all dhatus (Pole, 196).

Notes: This simple tasty drink is offered with respect to people of all ages who are killing themselves with overwork, drugs, alcohol, and worry.

HEART-FELT SMOOTHIE FOR PITTA AND KAPHA: Once you've made up the HEART-FELT TEA recipe, blend 1 cup of it with 2 Tablespoons soaked raw hemp seeds or sunflower seeds (see How to soak nuts or seeds for a single serving of a smoothie, p. 104). Add 1/2 - 1 cup fresh blueberries or ripe pear. Blend all ingredients until smooth.

Makes: 1 1/2 cups.

Effects: with blueberries, tridoshic. With pear, calms Pitta and Kapha, increases Vata if taken regularly.

This smoothie supports: heart, skin, plasma, muscle, mind.

OFF-THE-GRID HEART-FELT SMOOTHIE VARIATION: Make or bring the HEART-FELT TEA with you on the go. With a fork and a small bowl, mash together 1 banana or 1/2 - 1 cup fresh fruit with 1 – 2 Tablespoons unsweetened nut or seed butter. Gradually add 1 cup HEART-FELT TEA, whipping until smooth. Enjoy.

Note: The HEART FELT SMOOTHIE is a highly concentrated blend of anti-oxidants and rejuvenative herbs in an easy-to-absorb liquid package. We enjoyed this variation in the exquisite outback of Bears Ears National Monument in southeastern Utah.

"BITTER IS BETTER"
HEAL THAT SWEET TOOTH TEA

Time: 40 minutes
Makes: 1 quart

    1 Tablespoon organic fenugreek seeds
    1 teaspoon organic turmeric (or 1 Tablespoon grated, fresh turmeric root)
    1 Tablespoon organic burdock root
    1 teaspoon organic amalaki
    1 teaspoon organic guduchi
    6 cups water

Bring the water to a boil in a saucepan. Stir in all ingredients; simmer for 30 minutes or more uncovered. Strain and serve.

Effects: tridoshic in moderation. Excellent for Pitta and Kapha, could aggravate Vata if used daily.

This tea supports: blood sugar regulation, plasma, blood, skin, urinary tract, reproductive tissue.

Comments: This tea is appropriately bitter to cut through excess sweet, sugar in the blood, congestion, toxins, stagnation. It is an excellent beverage for diabetes, pre-diabetes, and lowering high glucose in healthy ways.

Notes: "Bitter is better" is a well-known saying from Dr. Vasant Lad to his students. We honor him here.

When using any cleansing or rejuvenative tea regularly, it's wise to be sure it's organic.

Contraindications: This drink is not appropriate for use in hypoglycemia.

EXTRA-STRENGTH VARIATION: Stir in 1 Tablespoon organic aloe vera juice (per cup of tea), when serving.

WOMAN'S YUM TEA *YEAR-ROUND*

This tasty rejuvenative beverage is appropriate for many occasions.

Time: 1 hour or more
Makes: 1 quart

  1 teaspoon organic shatavari
  1 teaspoon organic fenugreek seeds
  1 Tablespoon organic raspberry leaves
  1 Tablespoon organic rose petals
  6 cups of water

Bring the water to a boil in a saucepan. Stir in the shatavari and fenugreek; simmer uncovered for 15 minutes or more. Add the raspberry leaves and rose petals, turn off the heat, cover and steep at least 30 minutes. Strain, enjoy as it is, or add your choice of milk and sweetener (coconut sugar or honey).

Effects: tridoshic.

This tea supports: digestion, blood sugar regulation, reproductive tissue.

Comments: This rejuvenative tea supports women's sexual organs in many ways. It can be used with painful menstruation, amenorrhea, menopause, and perimenopause. It enhances fertility and strength. Actually, it is a fine rejuvenative for both sexes.

Notes: "Yum" refers to the sacred feminine in Tibetan. While this drink is not for use in pregnancy (due to the fenugreek) or for those avoiding estrogenic plants (shatavari), it is fine for lactation (see the following variation).

I emphasize organic here, because much of the Ayurvedic herbal marketplace is not yet organic. It's important if you're making a rejuvenative tea for it to be clear and whole.

MOM'S TEA: Add 1 teaspoon fennel seeds with the raspberry and rose, for an extra boost while breast feeding. This variation soothes digestion for both mom and baby.

EASY REJUVENATIVE SMOOTHIE: Once you've made a quart of this tea, simply follow the directions for the HEART-FELT SMOOTHIE, substituting WOMAN'S YUM TEA for the HEART-FELT TEA. Very tasty.

MAN'S YAB TEA *YEAR-ROUND*

Consider a vibrant and restorative drink that builds energy steadily.

Time: 1 hour or more
Makes: 1 quart

1 teaspooon organic ashwaganda
1 teaspoon organic shatavari
1 teaspoon organic fenugreek seeds
1 teaspooon organic kapikacchu (optional)
1 Tablespoon organic raw dandelion root
1 Tablespoon organic hibiscus flowers
6 cups of water

Bring the water to a boil in a saucepan. Stir in the ashwaganda, shatavari, fenugreek, kapikacchu, and dandelion root. Simmer uncovered for 15 minutes or more. Add the hibiscus flowers, remove from heat and steep covered for 30 minutes or more. Strain, enjoy as it is, or add your choice of milk and sweetener (coconut sugar or honey).

Effects: tridoshic.

This tea supports: blood sugar regulation, reproductive tissue.

Comments: This rasayana *(rejuvenative or restorative in Ayurveda) beverage enhances energy, stress relief, libido, and fertility. It also supports liver function and detoxification. While it is great for men, it is also safe and effective for women.*

Note: "Yab" refers to the sacred masculine in Tibetan. Again, organic is emphasized here for skillful rejuvenation.

DAD'S TEA: Add 1 teaspoon shankhapushi when you bring the herbs to simmer for 15 minutes. Good for soothing the nerves if you're the parent (or relative or friend) of a teenager, toddler, or independent-minded offspring.

RASAYANA SMOOTHIE: Once you've made a quart of this tea, simply follow the directions for the HEART-FELT SMOOTHIE, substituting MAN'S YAB TEA for the HEART-FELT TEA. Delicious.

LIVER DETOX TEA YEAR-ROUND

Time: 1 1/2 hours, plus an overnight soak
Makes: 2 quarts

    2 teaspoons organic raw dandelion root
    2 teaspoons organic burdock root
    6 cups water
    Another 6 cups water

Bring the first 6 cups of water to a boil in a saucepan. Stir in the herbs; boil for 1/2 hour uncovered. Remove from heat, strain the tea into quart glass jar, leaving the herbs in the saucepan. Add another 6 cups of water to the pot, bring to a boil again for 45 minutes. Cover and let sit overnight. In the morning, strain this second decoction into another quart glass jar. Store the tea in the fridge until needed. Drink one or more cups per day.

Effects: excellent for Pitta and Kapha, it can be taken up to three times per day with meals. It can aggravate Vata if used on a regular basis.

This detoxifying tea supports: digestion, elimination, liver, gall bladder, plasma, blood, skin, urinary tract.

Comments: It clears ama, stagnation and swollen lymph glands. It is diuretic. It is an excellent support if you're looking to switch from a high animal fat, high processed food diet to something lighter and cleaner.

Notes: This classic recipe comes from medical herbalist Lynn Childson of Santa Fe, New Mexico, who has supported this book with her knowledge and inspiration.

FAUX CHAYAVANPRASH TEA   *YEAR-ROUND*

Time: Initially, 30 minutes – time to make the mix plus time to infuse the tea with positive intention. Thereafter, 15 minutes per pot of tea.

Makes: the amount selected below.

Ingredients	for 2 cups	for 4 cups	for 8 cups	for 12 cups
water	3 cups	6 cups	3 quarts	4 quarts
amalaki	1 teaspoon	2 teaspoons	1 Tablespoon	2 Tablespoons
ashwagandha	1/2 teaspoon	1 teaspoon	2 teaspoons	1 Tablespoon
hawthorn berry	1/2 teaspoon	1 teaspoon	2 teaspoons	1 Tablespoon
guduchi	pinch	2 pinches	1/2 teaspoon	¾ teaspoon
manjishta	pinch	2 pinches	1/2 teaspoon	¾ teaspoon
grated fresh ginger	1 1/2 teaspoons	1 Tablespoon	2 Tablespoons	3 Tablespoons
cardamom	1/4 teaspoon	1/2 teaspoon	1 teaspoon	1 1/2 teaspoons

Boil the water, add the spices, and simmer for two minutes. Turn off the heat, cover and steep at least 10 minutes or more. After pouring, sweeten each cup with 1/2 tsp. raw honey (or sweetener of your choice) .

Effects: calms Vata and Kapha, neutral for Pitta.

Supports: plasma, blood, adrenals, reproduction, longevity, rejuvenation, ojas.

Note: I first started making up this tea when I wanted to offer the benefits of Chayavanprash, the classic Ayurvedic rasayana jam, without the presence of white sugar. A steady and popular beverage among my students and clients, it utilizes the deeply healing ingredients of the original formula, plus hawthorn berry.

Thanks to Deva Khalsa, www.devahealth.com, for her encouragement and support.

LEMON BALM CHAI *YEAR-ROUND*

This low-key tea is steadily soothing.

Time: 10 minutes
Serves: 4

2 Tablespoons organic lemon balm leaves, dry
1 teaspoon tulsi (whole leaves or powder)
1 Tablespoon lemongrass
1/4 teaspoon ground cinnamon
1/8 teaspoon nutmeg (freshly grated if possible)
1/16 teaspoon ground pippali
1 inch fresh ginger root, sliced into a few pieces
3 cups water
1 cup organic milk (I use unsweetened almond)
Sweetener to taste (I use 1 Tablespoon organic
   coconut sugar per pot)

Measure out the spices into a small bowl. Bring the water to a boil in a saucepan. Stir in the spices and simmer for 4 minutes. Pour the tea through a strainer into a clean container, pressing the spices against the strainer with a wooden spoon, to get as much as possible of their essence into the chai. Discard the spices. Put the tea back in the saucepan and add the milk. Heat until hot, yet not boiling. Sweeten to taste, even though our testers liked it without any sweetener at all! Serve hot or cool.

Effects: tridoshic.

This sattvic tea supports: mood!, nervous system, heart, immunity, ojas.

Notes: I (Amadea) keep trying to get this tea to make a statement. Yet it quietly sits in the corner of any party, just smiling. I notice I feel better after drinking it. Yet it's not a WoW kind of flavor. Sort of bodhisattva-like?

FIVE-SPICE MISO BROTH

This distinctive broth calms and satisfies.

Time: 5 minutes
Serves: 2 - 4

2 teaspoons organic light yellow miso (feel free to use a non-soy miso if you like)
1/8 teaspoon organic Five-spice powder
1 teaspoon ground coriander
2 cups water

Bring the water to a boil. Put the miso and spices in a 2- or 4-cup Pyrex measuring cup. Create a paste by adding a little water to the miso and the spices, stirring with a fork or wooden spoon. Add the rest of the hot water, stir well, serve.

Effects: calms Vata, neutral for Pitta and Kapha.

This broth supports: digestion, blood cells, muscles, hydration.

Note: Organic Five-spice powder can sometimes be found in natural groceries; it is available at www.mountainroseherbs.com *as Chinese 5 Spice Blend. It is a warming, digestive mix made from: star anise, cloves, cinnamon, Sichuan pepper, and fennel seeds. Here's a link to a DIY recipe:* https://www.thespruce.com/how-to-make-five-spice-powder-4065302

MAGIC YAM KHIR *YEAR-ROUND*

This golden looking elixir feels equally radiant in the belly.

Time: 25 – 30 minutes
Makes: 4 (1-cup) or 8 (1/2-cup) servings

1 pinch saffron (optional)
1 Tablespoon milk (almond or other)
2 Tablespoons ghee or organic coconut butter
1 small to medium yam (I use Jewel or Garnet,
    whichever is more colorful inside)
4 cups milk (almond or other)
1 inch fresh ginger (1 teaspoon grated)
1 inch fresh turmeric root (1 teaspoon grated)
    or 1 teaspoon ground turmeric
1/8 teaspoon ground cardamom or cinnamon
1 – 2 Tablespoons organic coconut sugar

If you use the saffron, soak it with the 1 Tablespoon milk in a cup for 10 minutes. Wash, peel and finely grate the yam. You'll need 1 cup total. With the same grater, finely grate the ginger and fresh turmeric; you'll need 1 teaspoon of each.

In a heavy, high-sided skillet over medium heat, melt the ghee or coconut butter. Add the ginger, turmeric and cardamom or cinnamon, then stir briefly, until aromatic. Add the grated yam and stir until it "wilts", a minute or two. Slowly stir the milk into the spiced yam mixture, then add the saffron and sugar. Turn up heat to medium high to bring the brew to a boil as you continue to stir the bottom to prevent sticking. Lower heat a little to simmer the mixture at a gentle boil for about 5 minutes. Remove from heat and cover until serving. Ladle into pretty cups and serve while warm.

Effects: calms Vata and Pitta. Add a pinch of dry ginger for Kapha.

This drink supports and most deeply nourishes every dhatu and ojas when made with ghee. With coconut butter, it supports plasma, nerves, immunity and ojas.

Notes: Thanks to Usha and Dr. Lad for their great cookbook, Ayurvedic Cooking for Self-Healing *with inspiration on this one. Cynthia Bancale's* GOLDEN MILK *in this cookbook also provided creative stimulus.*

THE *GUNAS*, THE *DOSHAS*, AND *AGNI*

Attribute/*Guna*	Calms the *dosha*, decreases:	Increases:
Heavy/*guru*	Vata, Pitta	Kapha
Light/*laghu*	Kapha	Vata, Pitta, and Agni
Slow, dull/*manda*	Vata, Pitta	Kapha
Sharp/*tikshna*	Kapha	Vata, Pitta
Cold/*shita*	Pitta	Vata, Kapha
Hot/*ushna*	Vata, Kapha	Pitta and Agni
Oily/*snigdha*	Vata and Agni	Pitta, Kapha
Dry/*ruksha*	Kapha, Pitta	Vata and Agni
Slimy/*shlakshna*	Vata and Agni	Pitta, Kapha
Rough/*khara*	Pitta, Kapha	Vata and Agni
Dense, concentrated/*sandra*	Vata, Pitta and Agni	Kapha
Liquid, dilute/*drava*	Vata and Agni	Pitta, Kapha
Soft/*mrudu*	Vata and Agni	Kapha, Pitta
Hard/*kathina*	Pitta and Agni	Vata, Kapha
Static, stable/*sthira*	Vata, Pitta and Agni	Kapha
Mobile/*chala*	Kapha	Vata, Pitta and Agni
Subtle/*sukshma*	Kapha	Vata, Pitta, and Agni
Gross/*sthula*	Vata, Pitta and Agni	Kapha
Clear/*vishada*	Kapha	Vata, Pitta and Agni
Cloudy/*avila*	Vata, Pitta and Agni	Kapha
Sticky/*picchila*	Vata, Pitta and Agni	Kapha

For more information on these traditional interpretations, see Lad, *Ayurveda: The Science of Self-Healing*

TASTES, *GUNAS* AND *DOSHAS*

Taste/*Rasa*: Elements	*Guna*	Effects on *Dosha & Agni*
Sweet/*madhura* Earth & Water	heavy, moist, cool, oily	Calms V & P Increases K Inhibits Agni
Sour/*amla* Earth & Fire	warm, moist, oily	Calms V Increases P & K Enhances Agni
Salty/*lavana* Water & Fire	moist, warm, heavy	Calms V Increases P & K Enhances Agni
Pungent, spicy/*katu* Fire & Air	hot, light, dry	Calms K Increases P & V Enhances Agni
Bitter/*tikta* Air & Ether	cold, light, dry	Calms P & K Increases V Enhances Agni via *samana vayu*
Astringent/*kashaya* Air & Earth	cool, dry, heavy	Calms P & K Increases V Inhibits Agni

For more information, see Sharma, *Introduction to Dravyaguna*

PLAY WITH DARK LEAFY GREENS

You can improvise with these nourishing veggies! This is Amadea's CHEAT SHEET to adapt recipes for different doshas and needs, by using specific plants.   **KEY**: "-" = calms, "+" = aggravates, "0" = neutral effect

All of the dark leafy greens are rich in magnesium, calcium, iron, beta-carotenes, and folate. Cooking them usually makes them easier for Vata to handle. Raw is fine for Pitta & Kapha, if well tolerated. Each has a unique blend of tastes and qualities

Food	Taste	Effect on Dosha	Other Info
arugula	pungent	-V, +P, -K	
asian greens	astringent, bitter	+V, -P, -K	
beet greens	astringent, sweet	+V, -P, -K	oxalic acid binds calcium
bok choy	astringent	+V, -P, -K	
cilantro	sweet, astringent	tridoshic	may help detoxify mercury
collards	bitter, astringent	+V, -P, -K	
comfrey leaf	sweet, astringent	+V, -P, -K	
dandelion greens	bitter	+V, -P, -K	supports liver
kale	bitter, astringent	+V, -P, -K	
lettuce	astringent, sweet (sometimes bitter)	+V, -P, -K	nervine
mache	sweet, astringent	0V, - P, -K	
mustard greens	pungent	- V, +P, -K	
nettles	astringent	+V, - P, -K	tonifying to kidneys & adrenals
parsley	pungent	- V, +P, -K	potent diuretic
sorrel	sour	-V, +P, +K (in excess)	oxalic acid
spinach (raw)	astringent, pungent	- V, - P, -K	Avoid spinach if kidney or gallstones
spinach (cooked)	astringent, sour	-V, +P, -K	oxalic acid binds calcium
swiss chard	astringent, sweet	+V, - P, - K	oxalic acid binds calcium
turnip greens	bitter, astringent	+V, -P, -K	

REMEMBER ABOUT THE SIX TASTES:

* Vata is calmed by **sweet**, **sour** and **salty** tastes (= all moistening and heavy).
* Kapha is balanced by **pungent**, **bitter** and **astringent** tastes (= all light).
* Pitta is most supported by **sweet**, **bitter** and **astringent** tastes (= all cooling).

Since we have all three doshas, we need all six tastes – yet in different proportions depending on our make-up.

Glossary

agni: digestive fire, sacred fire

alkalizing: substance that promotes a pH greater than 7, cleansing

ama: undigested wastes creating toxins in the body

amla: sour, one of the six therapeutic tastes

anupana: a substance that carries the medicinal qualities of herbs into the tissues, like milk, honey, ghee, or aloe vera

aphrodisiac (*vajikaran*): healing and strengthening for the reproductive organs, increases sexual interest

asthi: bone tissue, one of the *dhatus*

astringent (*kashaya*): cold, light contractive taste, calming to *Pitta* and *Kapha*

Ayurveda: the science of life

bitter (*tikta*): cooling, light, dry taste supportive to digestion and cleansing; calms *Pitta* and *Kapha*

decoction: a tea that is boiled slowly for 15 – 20 minutes, often made of roots, barks, or large seeds. (Moore)

dhatu: one of the seven or eight essential tissues of the body, including *rasa, rakta, mamsa, meda, asthi, majja, artava, shukra*

diuretic: increases urination

dosha: one of three biological energies - *Vata, Pitta,* and *Kapha* - that sustain life and metabolism and determine one's constitution.

drava: liquid

edema: water retention, results in swelling

electrolyte: vital minerals, including sodium, potassium, calcium, and magnesium

guna: one of 21 paired attributes or qualities. Examples are hot & cold, light & heavy, dry & oily.

infusion: A tea made by pouring boiling water over a plant, particularly more delicate leaves, flowers, and small seeds. (Moore)

Kapha: the *dosha* arising from earth and water; heavy, cool, moist, steady/stable

karma: effect, action

kashaya: astringent, one of the six therapeutic tastes; also, an extract

katu: pungent, one of the six therapeutic tastes

lavana: salty, one of the six therapeutic tastes

laxative: promotes elimination through bowel movements

madhura: sweet, one of the six therapeutic tastes

mahaguna: one of the three great qualities of mind - sattva, rajas, and tamas

majja: nerve, bone marrow, and fascia tissue; one of the seven *dhatus*

malas: bodily waste products - urine, feces, perspiration

meda: fat tissue, one of the *dhatus*

nirama: condition free of *ama* or toxins

nervine: strengthens and supports the nerves, *majja*

nutritive: provides nourishment for the body; rich in nutrition

ojas: vital energy cushion of the body; supports immunity

Pitta: the *dosha* arising from fire and water; hot, sharp, oily, light, liquid

prabhava: the specific action or special potency of a substance, beyond any general rules that apply to it

pranayama: healing breathing processes

prakruti: birth constitution

prana: mobile vital energy absorbed through breath and food; chi

prasad: blessed food

pungent (*katu*): hot, light taste; calming to *Kapha*

rajas: mental quality of assertion, aggression, warm energy and action; one of the 3 *mahagunas*

rakta: red blood cells; one of the *dhatus*

rasa: taste perceived in the mouth; the six tastes of sweet, sour, salty, pungent, bitter, and astringent; one of the *dhatus*, plasma, the liquid part of the blood; also, feeling, emotion

rasayana: rejuvenative, restorative, revitalizing

salty (*lavana*): warm, heavy taste, calming to *Vata*

sama: condition with *ama* or toxins

sattva: mental quality of love, calm, clarity, harmony, balance; one of the 3 *mahagunas*

shukra: reproductive tissue, can apply generally to both sexes, yet often refers only to male reproductive tissue; one of the *dhatus*

sour (*amla*): warm; acidic taste; calming to *Vata*

srota: essential channel for the movement of energy and metabolism in the body; the *dhatus* have channel manifestations, as in *rasavaya srotas*, the channel for plasma

sweet (*madhura*): cool, heavy taste, calming to *Vata* and *Pitta*

tamas: mental quality of contraction, grounding, resistance, inertia, habitual patterns; one of the 3 *mahagunas*

taste: see *rasa*

tejas: warm, vital creative energy, transmitted thru *ojas* to the digestive tract

tridosha: the three doshas of *Vata*, *Pitta*, and *Kapha*

tridoshic: balancing for all three *doshas*

Vata: the biological energy, *dosha*, arising from air and space/ether; dry, cool, light, mobilev

vikruti: the current condition, imbalance

vipak: the final, post-digestive effect of taste impacting the metabolism of the whole body

virya: energy, energetic effect of taste on the digestive tract, as in warming or cooling

Resources for Learning and Healing

Online Information about *Easy Healing Drinks* and Amadea Morningstar

Easy Healing Drinks from the Wisdom of Ayurveda can be found at www.easyhealingdrinks.com. Amadea offers information on how to apply this wisdom more deeply in life. Her blogs, videos, and schedule can be found at www.amadeamorningstart.net, along with links to reliable sources of ingredients.

Take NAMA-certified PACE (continuing education) courses and other courses with Amadea http://www.AyurvedaPolarityYoga.com. Go to "The Institute", "Classes".

More Education and Ayurveda Supplies

The Ayurvedic Institute http://www.ayurveda.com/
Enjoy an extensive library of free Friday night lectures from Dr. Vasant Lad.

National Ayurvedic Medical Association http://www.ayurvedanama.org/
Find Ayurvedic professionals in your area; connect with colleagues.

The Ayurveda Journal of Health http://ajh-journal.com/
Write, read, and discover more about Ayurveda in this fine professional journal.

On Line Constitutional Questionnaire http://www.banyanbotanicals.com
Discover your Ayurvedic constitution with this reliable interactive tool.

The work of Dr. Alakananda Ma https://www.alandiashram.org/
This inspired school offers the only 4-year Doctor of Ayurveda program in the U.S.

The Ayurveda Experience https://www.theayurvedaexperience.com/
Get a wide range of online courses from top-notch Ayurvedic teachers.

Dr. David Frawley https://www.vedanet.com/
A master teacher of Ayurveda makes available a broad range of Vedic courses.

Dr. John Douillard's Life Spa http://lifespa.com/
View numerous clear, insightful educational videos from Dr. Douillard.

Cate Stillman, yogahealer https://yogahealer.com/podcasts/
Enjoy highly educational podcast interviews with dynamo Cate Stillman.

Ayur Botanicals https://www.ayurbotanicals.com.au/
Find courses, podcasts, consults, and Ayurvedic supplies in Australia.

Ayurvedic Cooking Courses in France https://www.mapetitecuisinesaine.com/
Explore Europe and Ayurveda with Michele Schulz, holistic Ayurvedic chef.

Diamond Way Ayurveda http://www.diamondwayayurveda.com/
Integrate traditional Indian & Tibetan healing and skills with Melanie & Robert Sachs.

Lotus Ayurveda http://lotusayurveda.com/
Receive care, education & herbs, directed by senior Ayurvedic consultant Cynthia Copple.

Dr. Claudia Welch https://drclaudiawelch.com/
Dr. Welch and colleague Dr. Robert Svoboda share inspired education and resources.

California College of Ayurveda https://www.vedanet.com/
Study at one of the oldest Ayurveda schools in the U.S.

Wise Earth School of Ayurveda http://wiseearth.com/
Absorb the spiritual healing of Ayurvedic pioneer Bri Maya Tiwari.

Deva Khalsa http://devahealth.com/
Train and cleanse with Deva Khalsa, skilled Ayurvedic practitioner in Santa Fe, NM.

Dr. Anisha Durve https://www.anisha.guru/
Connect with wisdom & essential oils for women from this talented author & healer.

Talya's Kitchen https://www.talyaskitchen.com/
Vegan and Ayurvedic? Meet the courses of Talya Lutzker.

Joyful Belly http://www.joyfulbelly.com/
Discover numerous great ideas for healthy food prep.

Fine Suppliers of High Quality Organic Herbs and Spices

Banyan Botanicals http://www.banyanbotanicals.com

Mountain Rose Herbs https://www.mountainroseherbs.com/

Organic India teas https://www.organicindiashop.com/

India http://apeda.gov.in/apedawebsite/organic/Organic_Products.htm

Pukka Herbs https://www.pukkaherbs.com/

About Inline Citations: Each citation in *Easy Healing Drinks* gives an author and a page number, ex: (Tirtha, 134). All citations can be found in the **Books** list that follows. This example relates to Tirtha's *The Ayurveda Encyclopedia*, page 134.

Books

Drikung Kagyu H.E. Garchen Rinpoche, *The Commentary on the Essential Meaning of the Thirty-Seven Practices of Bodhisattvas*, 2011 (Singapore)

Frawley, David, *Ayurvedic Healing: A Comprehensive Guide*, 1989

Jaffrey, Madhur, *An Invitation to Indian Cooking*, 1973

—— *At Home with Madhur Jaffrey*, 2010

—— *Madhur Jaffrey's Quick & Easy Indian Cooking*, 2007

—— *Vegetarian India*, 2015

Johari, Harish, *The Healing Cuisine*, 1994

Joshi, Sunil, *Ayurveda & Panchakarma*, 1997

Kennedy, Diana, *The Cuisines of Mexico*, 1989

Lad, Usha & Vasant, *Ayurvedic Cooking for Self-Healing*, 1994

Lad, Vasant, *Ayurveda: The Science of Self-Healing*, 1984

—— *Textbook of Ayurveda*, vols. 1 – 3, 2002 to present

Lad, Vasant & David Frawley, *The Yoga of Herbs*, 1986

Miller, Light & Bryan, *Ayurveda & Aromatherapy*, 1995

Moore, Michael, *Medicinal Plants of the Mountain West*, 1979

Morningstar, Amadea, *The Ayurvedic Guide to Polarity Therapy: Hands-on Healing*, 2001

—— *Ayurvedic Cooking for Westerners*, 1995

Morningstar, Amadea with Urmila Desai, *The Ayurvedic Cookbook*, 1990

Nagral, Kumud S., *Ayurveda for Modern Medical Practitioners*, 2008 (India)

O'Donnell, Kate, *The Everyday Ayurveda Cookbook*, 2015

Packard, Candis Cantin, *Pocket Guide to Ayurvedic Healing*, 1996

Pole, Sebastian, *Ayurvedic Medicine*, 2006

Rao, Rupen & Aparna Pattewar, *ayurveda cookbook*, 2015

Shanbhag, Vivek, *A Beginner's Introduction to Ayurvedic Medicine*, 1994

Sharma, P.V., *Introduction to Dravyaguna*, (Indian Pharmacology), 1976 (India)

Tirtha, Swami Sada Shiva, *The Ayurveda Encyclopedia*, 1998

Tiwari, Bri Maya, *A Life of Balance*, 1995

Welch, Claudia, *Balance Your Hormones, Balance Your Life*, 2011

Wood, Matthew, *The Book of Herbal Wisdom, Using Plants as Medicines*, 1997

Texts available in the USA unless noted in parentheses.

Acknowledgments

We deeply appreciate everyone who joined us on this journey, Dr. Vasant Lad, our design, layout and editing teams, our recipe testers and their loved ones. Many people helped in different ways, including our blessed families. I, Amadea, especially appreciate Renee Lynn for catalyzing this process. Renee came up with the idea of a healing drinks book and proceeded to help bring it to life with her glorious sun-lit photographs.

Dr. Vasant Lad, master Ayurvedic physician at the Ayurvedic Institute, looked at my Vedic chart in 2014 and encouraged me to write again. He also offered a direct experience of how to heal deeply with Ayurveda, for which I am most grateful.

Cynthia Bancale designed the book with skill, patience and a fine appreciation for balance and color. Michele Schulz was ceaselessly supportive with copy editing and perceptive insights. The professional team of Karen Bomm, Mary Neighbour and Leslie Waltzer worked together with seamless excellence to bring this print book to birth. Elizabeth Carovillano guided us in spring with creative verve, including the lively spring and summer graphs. Tim Davis gave us our first keen-eyed edit, took the authors' photo (and much more). The support of Margie Noren, Gordon Bruen and Iza Bruen-Morningstar was deeply felt.

Our recipe testers gave their time and feedback generously: Lian & Tim Blair, Shruthi Bajaj, Katie Bromberg, Chelsea Call, Doug Conwell, Sulis Cutler, Brenda deMartine, Alyiah Doughty, Connie Fisher, Gwendolyn Henzi, Melissa Ireland, Lori Johnson, Deva Khalsa, Carry Kim, Pascale Million, Manon C. Pierme, Stephanie Rogers, Ina Rucker, Nancy Schmitz, Manjula Spears, Ralph Steele, Alex Stoller, Priscilla Stuckey, Maureen Sutton, Sarah McDaniel Valencia, the Wagner-Hiesters, Tess Wilkes & Dhiru Paulraj, and Marguerite Wilson. Many of the above recipe testers studied with me in the Ayurvedic Self Care Educators program (ASCE) at APTYI from 2007 – 2014. I bless and honor you.

We thank Susan Contreras, Brian duBoff, Kitchen Angels, Tony McCarty, Mignon Ohmura, Gay Patterson, Angela Werneke, Michele Herling, and Kendra Arnold for their technical excellence. We thank Tim Gaucher, Margie Noren, Aimee Putnam, and Ralph Steele for sharing their stories with us.

Within our healing community, the work of Dr. Alakananda Ma, Anuj Agarwal, Banyan Botanicals, Lenny Blank, Patricia Tuttle Brown, Dolores Chiappone, Lynn Childson, Cynthia Copple, Jennifer Eddinger, Dr. David Frawley & Shambhavi Chopra, my colleagues at East-West Healing Arts, Dr. Eric Grasser, Dr. Sharada Hall, Herbs Etc., Drs. Sunil & Shalmali Joshi, Deva Khalsa, Tesia Love, Dr. Diana Lurie, Talya Lutzker, Shanna Marsh Martinez, Dr. McKenzie Myers, Sebastian Pole, Melanie & Robert Sachs, Gina Sager, Cate Stillman, Dr. Frederic Verswijver, Susan & Larry Weis-Bohlen, and Wynn Werner inspires us.

I am grateful for my root teachers, HE Garchen Rinpoche, HH Chetsang Rinpoche, Traga Rinpoche, Khandro Rinpoche, and Tulku Nyima Gyaltsen Rinpoche, and my Dharma companions at Rigdzin Dharma in Albuquerque, New Mexico and Garchen Buddhist Institute in Arizona. I thank the Kuonis, Norens, and Stonesifers, and all the clients and students who've taught me so much.

Index

Amadea Morningstar (left) and Renee Lynn (right)

About the Authors

Amadea Morningstar is the author (with Urmila Desai) of the best-selling classic *The Ayurvedic Cookbook*. Her Ayurveda blog has been named among the top ones on the web www.amadeamorningstar.net/blog. She has been writing and teaching about Ayurveda since the early 1980s. Her commitment is to bring alive this precious and ancient natural healing science in simple, clear and affordable ways for the benefit of as many people as possible, and for the benefit of the earth which nourishes us.

Renee Lynn, a professional photographer, embraced this project because of her deep interest in the healing wisdom of Ayurveda. Though mainly known for her wildlife photography, she has previously photographed three cookbooks. For the images in this book it was her intent to include the beautiful New Mexico landscape as a backdrop and the healing element of the sun as the sole light source. Creating the images with the natural elements really brought the recipes to life. May they be enjoyed in good health and happiness!

Enjoy more from Amadea!

The Ayurvedic Cookbook

Apply Ayurvedic principles to your life and cooking with hundreds of delicious, easy, seasonal recipes, keyed for your constitution. This healing classic puts the keys to good health and ancient wisdom in your hands. Learn Ayurveda in your own kitchen, with great tasting East Indian foods from Amadea and Gujarati chef, Urmila Desai.

El libro de cocina ayurvédica
(Spanish edition of The Ayurvedic Cookbook)

Este libro nos brinda una nueva perspectiva sobre el arte milenario de Ayurveda. Incluye más de 250 recetas probadas y degustadas, diseñadas éspecificamente para equilibrar cada constitución.

Easy Healing Drinks from the Wisdom of Ayurveda
Delicious and Nourishing Winter Recipes

Get the same great WINTER recipes and images in Easy Healing Drinks in an affordable one-season ebook format that can be downloaded to your computer, phone, or ebook reader. This exclusive offer is available only at:
www.easyhealingdrinks.com

   www.AmadeaMorningstar.net

Easy Healing Drinks from the Wisdom of Ayurveda

Cleansing and Sustaining Recipes

Get the same great SPRING recipes and photos in *Easy Healing Drinks* in an affordable one-season ebook format that can be downloaded to your computer, phone, or ebook reader. Also includes the foreword from Dr. Vasant Lad and insights on summer healing. This exclusive offer is available only at:

www.easyhealingdrinks.com

Ayurvedic Cooking for Westerners

Enjoy over 200 fast nourishing recipes for healthful living, prepared with ingredients easily available in the West. Learn how to cook fresh, including recipes for specific illnesses, like allergies and candida. This Ayurveda cookbook is popular with single people, families, and those who like tasty, delicious, digestible familiar food.

The Ayurvedic Guide to Polarity Therapy

Deepen your understanding of how to cleanse and build with both Ayurveda and Polarity Therapy. Directly and easily apply well-organized information about rejuvenating the dhatus with food, herbs and movement naturally. This is a great companion volume to Easy Healing Drinks, with many specific healing foods and herbs for each dhatu.

May this work benefit all living beings.